Bond
No.1 for exam success

Non-verbal Reasoning

Assessment Papers

9–10 years

Book 1

OXFORD
UNIVERSITY PRESS

OXFORD
UNIVERSITY PRESS

Great Clarendon Street, Oxford, OX2 6DP, United Kingdom

Oxford University Press is a department of the University of Oxford.
It furthers the University's objective of excellence in research,
scholarship, and education by publishing worldwide. Oxford is
a registered trade mark of Oxford University Press in the UK and in
certain other countries

British Library Cataloguing in Publication Data
Data available

978-0-19-277647-1

10 9 8 7 6 5 4 3 2

Paper used in the production of this book is a natural, recyclable
product made from wood grown in sustainable forests.
The manufacturing process conforms to the environmental
regulations of the country of origin.

Printed in China

Acknowledgements

The publishers would like to thank the following for permissions to
use copyright material:

Page make-up: OKS Prepress, India
Illustrations: Wearset Ltd
Cover illustrations: Lo Cole

Although we have made every effort to trace and contact all
copyright holders before publication this has not been possible in all
cases. If notified, the publisher will rectify any errors or omissions at
the earliest opportunity.

Links to third party websites are provided by Oxford in good faith
and for information only. Oxford disclaims any responsibility for
the materials contained in any third party website referenced in
this work.

Before you get started

What is Bond?

This book is part of the Bond Assessment Papers series for non-verbal reasoning, which provides a **thorough and progressive course in non-verbal reasoning** from ages six to twelve. It builds up non-verbal reasoning skills from book to book over the course of the series.

What does this book cover and how can it be used to prepare for exams?

Non-verbal reasoning questions can be grouped into four distinct groups: identifying shapes, missing shapes, rotating shapes, coded shapes and logic. *Non-verbal Reasoning 9–10 years Book 1* and *Book 2* practise a wide range of questions appropriate to the age group drawn from all these categories. The papers can be used both for general practice and as part of the run-up to 11+ and other selective exams. One of the key features of Bond Assessment Papers is that each one practises **a very wide variety of skills and question types** so that children are always challenged to think – and don't get bored repeating the same question type again and again. We believe that variety is the key to effective learning. It helps children 'think on their feet' and cope with the unexpected: it is surprising how often children come out of non-verbal reasoning exams having met question types they have not seen before.

What does the book contain?

- **6 papers** – each one contains 54 questions.

- **Tutorial links throughout** – 📖 – this icon appears in the margin next to the questions. It indicates links to the relevant section in *How to do 11+ Non-verbal Reasoning*, our invaluable subject guide that offers explanations and practice for all core question types.

- **Scoring devices** – there are score boxes at the end of each paper and a Progress Chart on page 64. The chart is a visual and motivating way for children to see how they are doing. It also turns the score into a percentage that can help decide what to do next.

- **Next Steps Planner** – advice on what to do after finishing the papers can be found on the inside back cover.

- **Answers** – located in an easily-removed central pull-out section.

How can you use this book?

One of the great strengths of Bond Assessment Papers is their flexibility. They can be used at home, in school and by tutors to:

- set **timed formal practice** tests – allow about 40 minutes per paper. Reduce the suggested time limit by five minutes to practise working at speed.

- provide **bite-sized chunks** for regular practice

- **highlight strengths and weaknesses** in the core skills

- identify **individual needs**

- set **homework**

- follow a **complete 11⁺ preparation strategy** alongside *The Parents' Guide to the 11⁺* (see below).

It is best to start at the beginning and work through the papers in order. If you are using the book as part of a careful run-in to the 11⁺, we suggest that you also have two other essential Bond resources close at hand:

How to do 11⁺ Non-verbal Reasoning: the subject guide that explains all the question types practised in this book. Use the cross-reference icons to find the relevant sections.

The Parents' Guide to the 11⁺: the step-by-step guide to the whole 11⁺ experience. It clearly explains the 11⁺ process, provides guidance on how to assess children, helps you to set complete action plans for practice and explains how you can use *Non-verbal Reasoning 9–10 years Book 1* and *Book 2* as part of a strategic run-in to the exam.

See the inside front cover for more details of these books.

What does a score mean and how can it be improved?

It is unfortunately impossible to predict how a child will perform when it comes to the 11⁺ (or similar) exam if they achieve a certain score on any practice book or paper. Success on the day depends on a host of factors, including the scores of the other children sitting the test. However, we can give some guidance on what a score indicates and how to improve it.

If children colour in the Progress Chart on page 64, this will give an idea of present performance in percentage terms. The Next Steps Planner inside the back cover will help you to decide what to do next to help a child progress. It is always valuable to go over wrong answers with children. If they are having trouble with any particular question type, follow the tutorial links to *How to do 11⁺ Non-verbal Reasoning* for step-by-step explanations and further practice.

Don't forget the website . . . !

Visit www.bond11plus.co.uk for lots of advice, information and suggestions on everything to do with Bond, the 11⁺ and helping children to do their best.

Paper 1

Which is the odd one out? Circle the letter.

Example

a   b   ⓒ   d   e

1

a   b   c   d   e

2

a   b   c   d   e

3

a   b   c   d   e

4

a   b   c   d   e

5

a   b   c   d   e

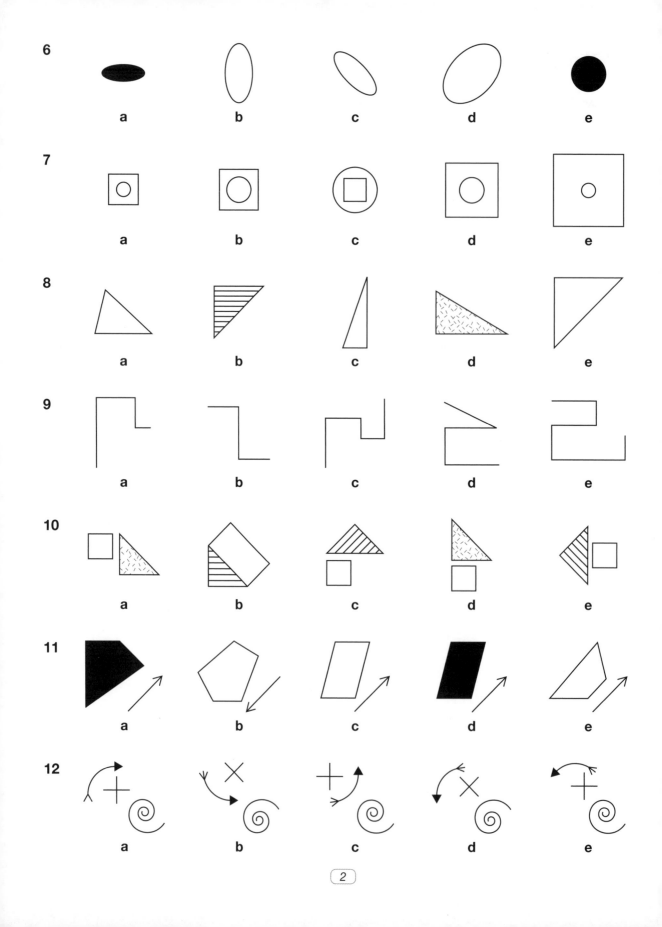

Which one comes next? Circle the letter.

Example

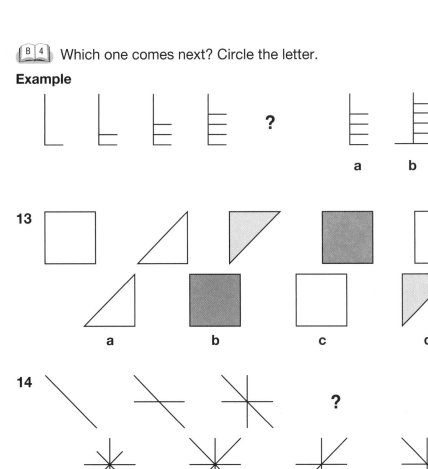

13

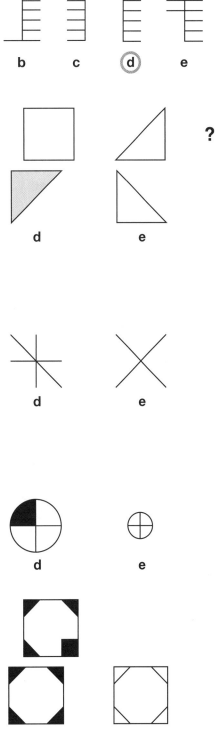

14

15

16

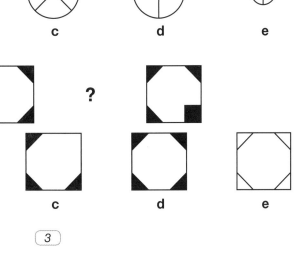

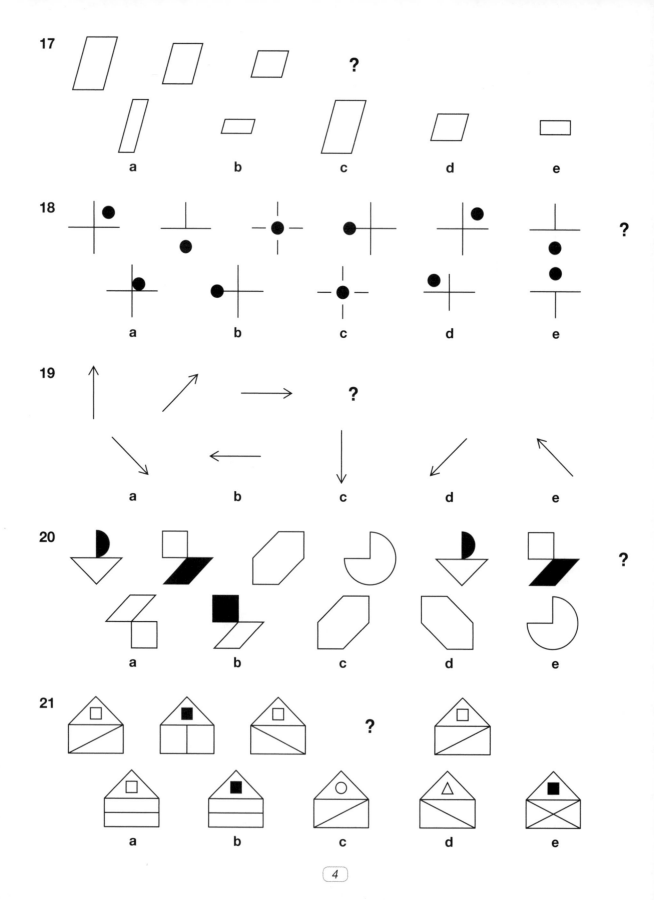

22

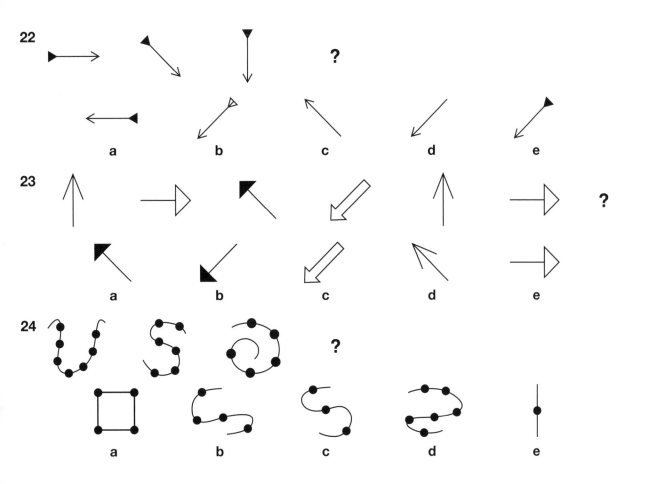

23

24

B 3 Which shape or pattern on the right completes the second pair in the same way as the first pair? Circle the letter.

Example

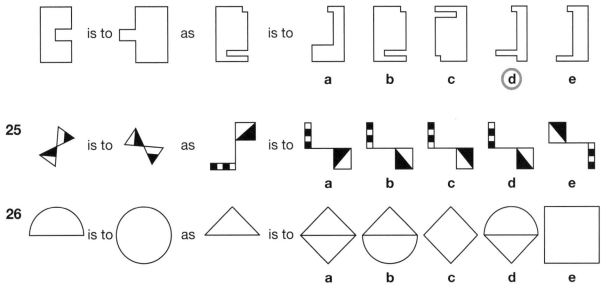

25

26

5

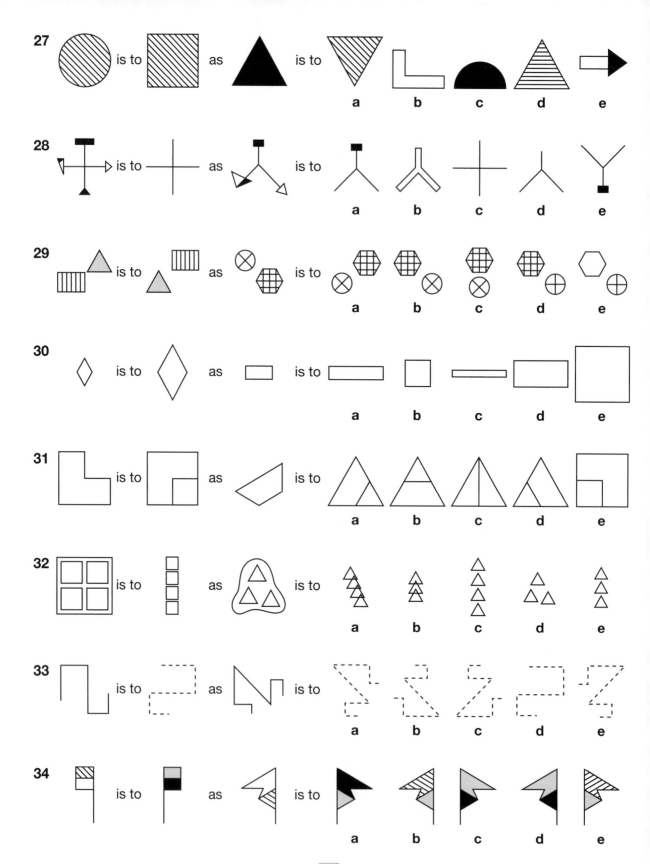

27

28

29

30

31

32

33

34

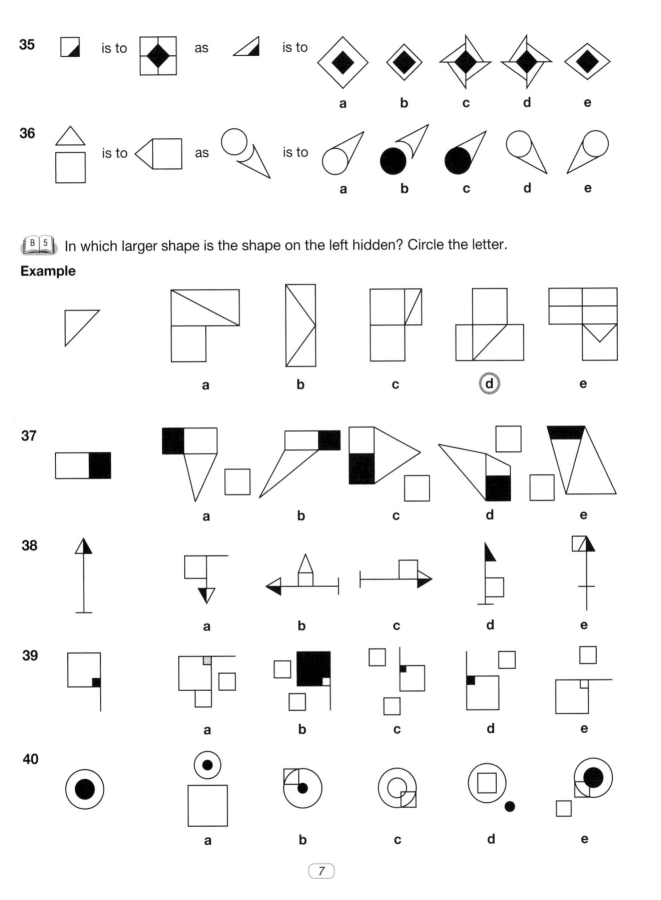

35

36

B 5 In which larger shape is the shape on the left hidden? Circle the letter.

Example

a   b   c   d   e

37

a   b   c   d   e

38

a   b   c   d   e

39

a   b   c   d   e

40

a   b   c   d   e

7

41

a

b

c

d

e

42

a

b

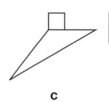
c

d

e

B 7 Which shape on the right is the reflection of the shape given on the left? Circle the letter.

Example

a

b

c

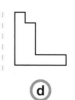
d

e

43

a

b

c

d

e

44

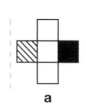
a

b

c

d

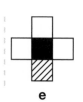
e

45

a

b

c

d

e

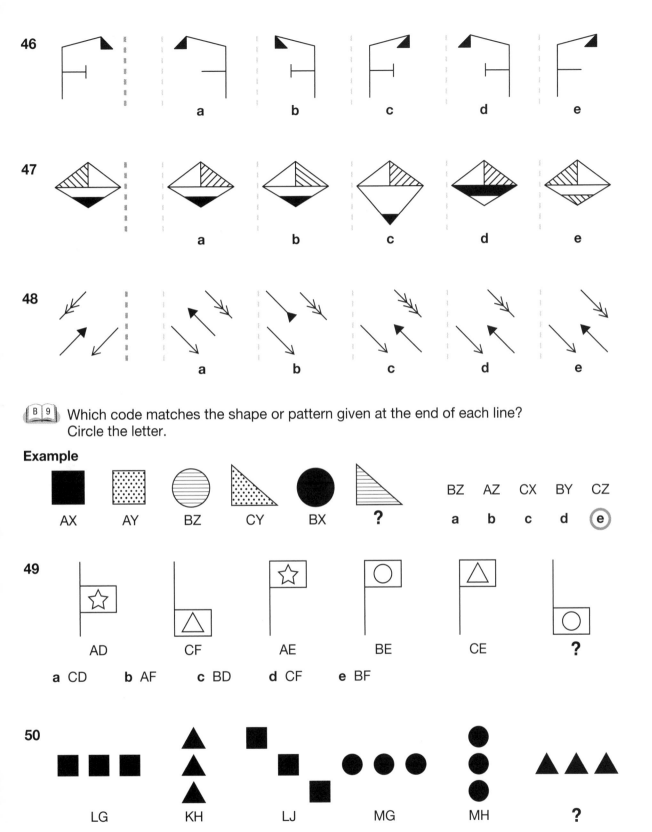

46

a b c d e

47

a b c d e

48

a b c d e

B 9 Which code matches the shape or pattern given at the end of each line?
Circle the letter.

Example

AX   AY   BZ   CY   BX   **?**

BZ   AZ   CX   BY   CZ
a   b   c   d   e

49

AD   CF   AE   BE   CE   **?**

a CD   b AF   c BD   d CF   e BF

50

LG   KH   LJ   MG   MH   **?**

a KH   b KG   c MJ   d KJ   e LH

51

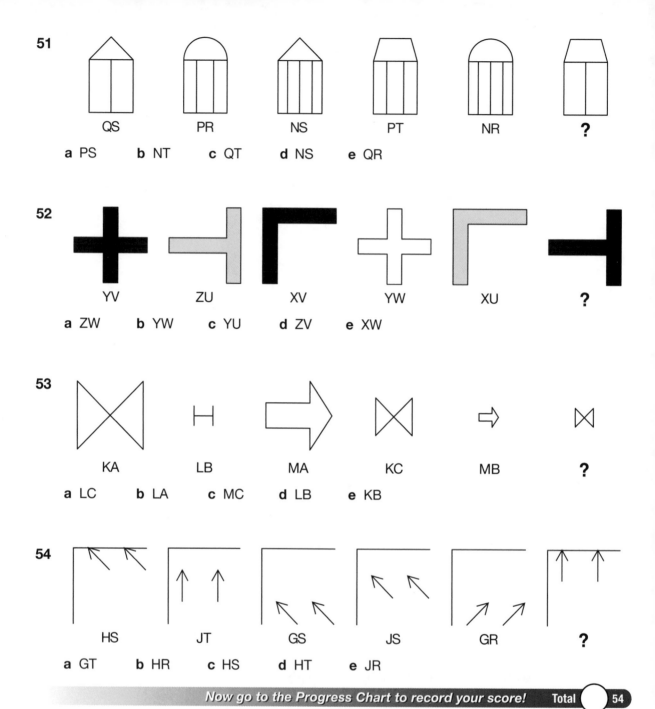

QS	PR	NS	PT	NR	**?**

a PS   **b** NT   **c** QT   **d** NS   **e** QR

52

YV	ZU	XV	YW	XU	**?**

a ZW   **b** YW   **c** YU   **d** ZV   **e** XW

53

KA	LB	MA	KC	MB	**?**

a LC   **b** LA   **c** MC   **d** LB   **e** KB

54

HS	JT	GS	JS	GR	**?**

a GT   **b** HR   **c** HS   **d** HT   **e** JR

Now go to the Progress Chart to record your score!   Total   54

Paper 2

Which is the odd one out? Circle the letter.

Example

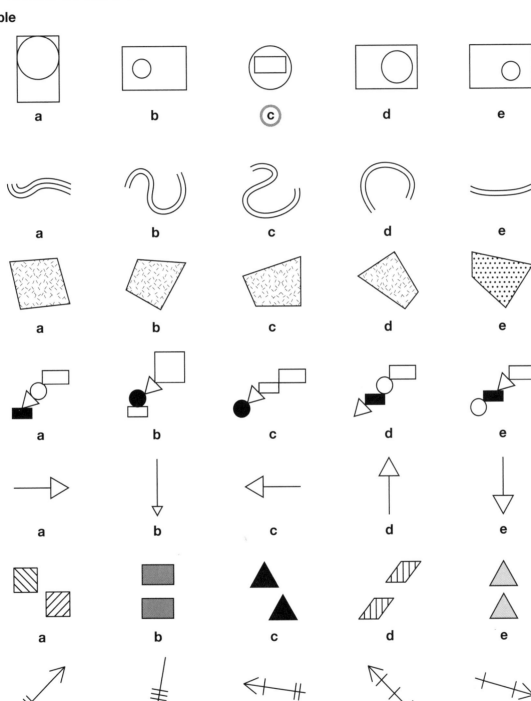

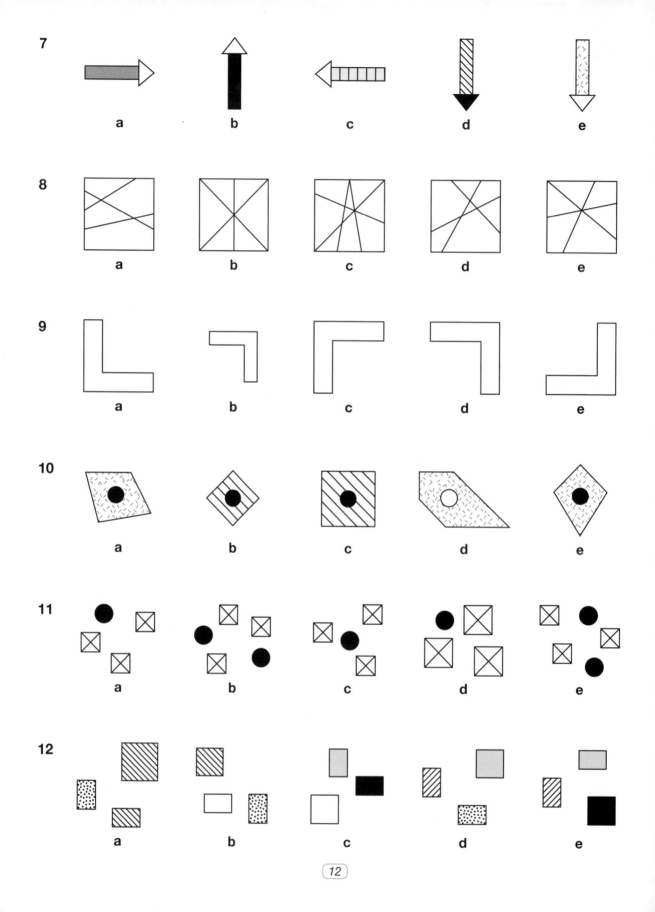

Which one comes next? Circle the letter.

Example

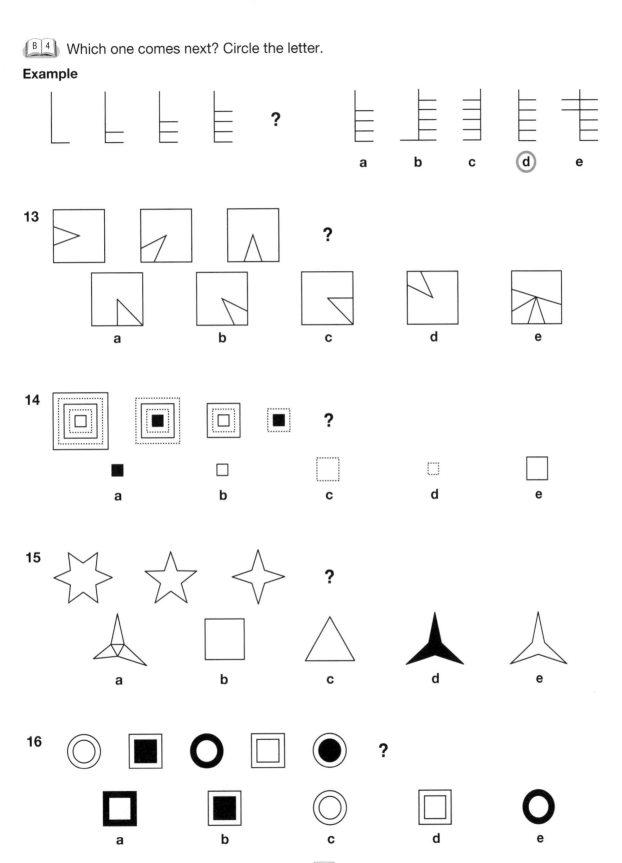

13

14

15

16

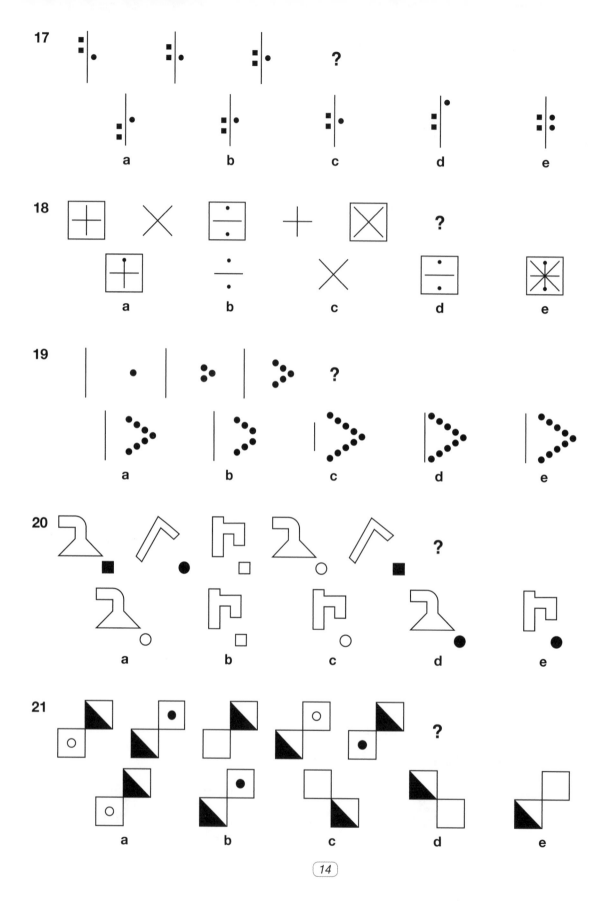

22

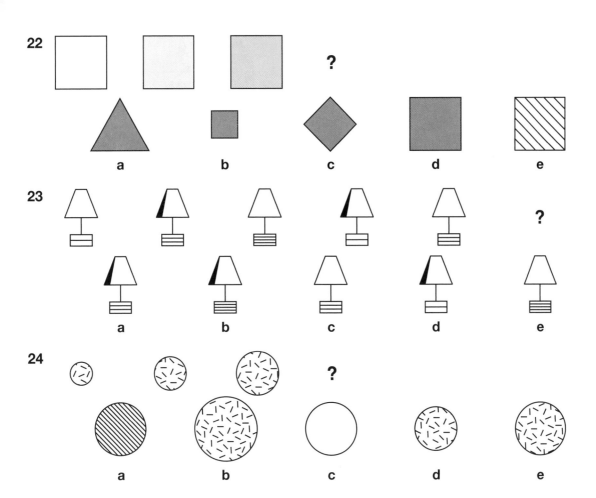

23

24

Which shape or pattern on the right completes the second pair in the same way as the first pair? Circle the letter.

Example

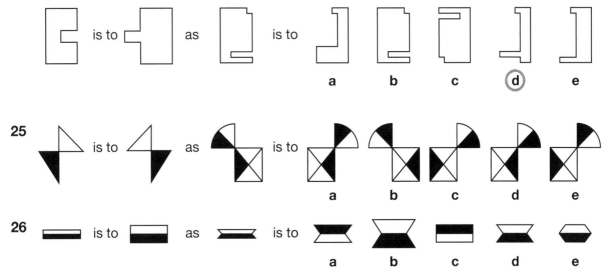

25

26

15

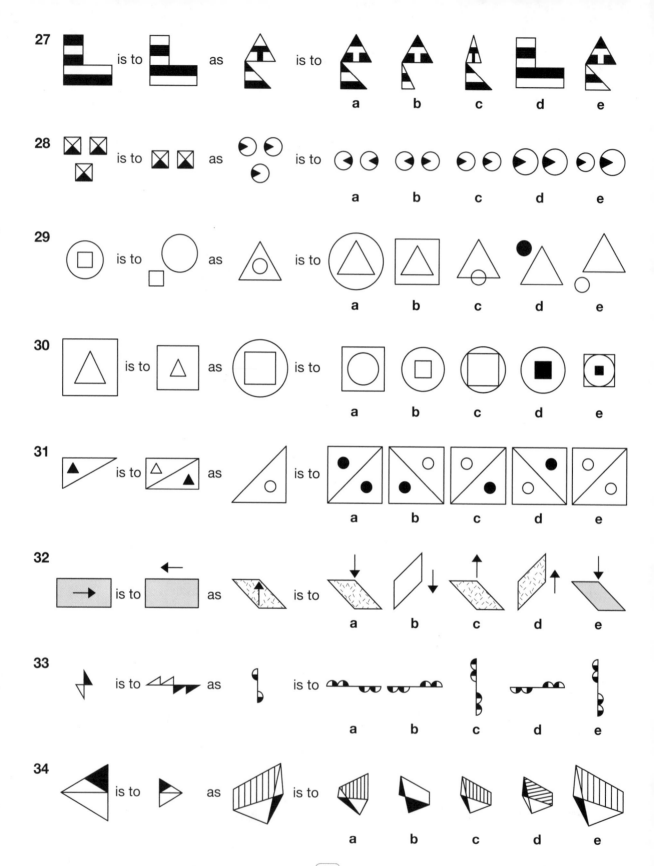

35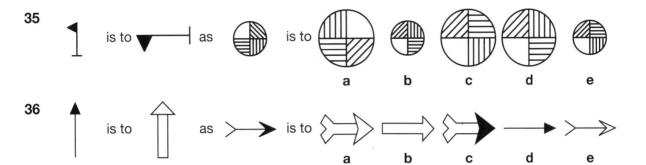

36

B 5 In which larger shape is the shape on the left hidden? Circle the letter.

Example

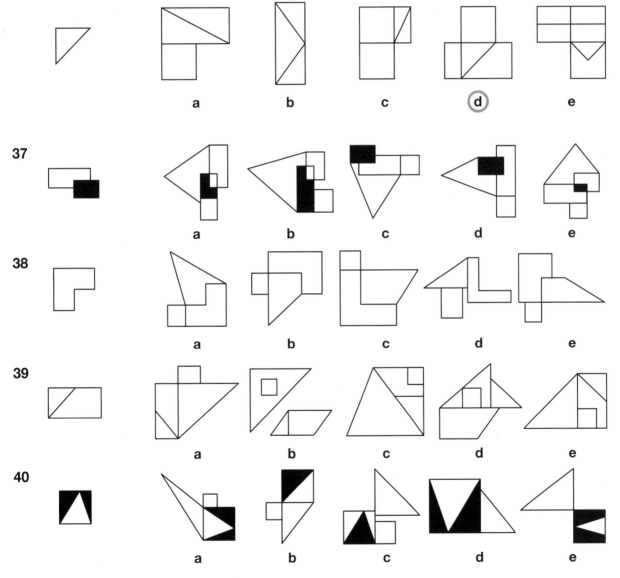

a   b   c   d   e

37

a   b   c   d   e

38

a   b   c   d   e

39

a   b   c   d   e

40

a   b   c   d   e

41

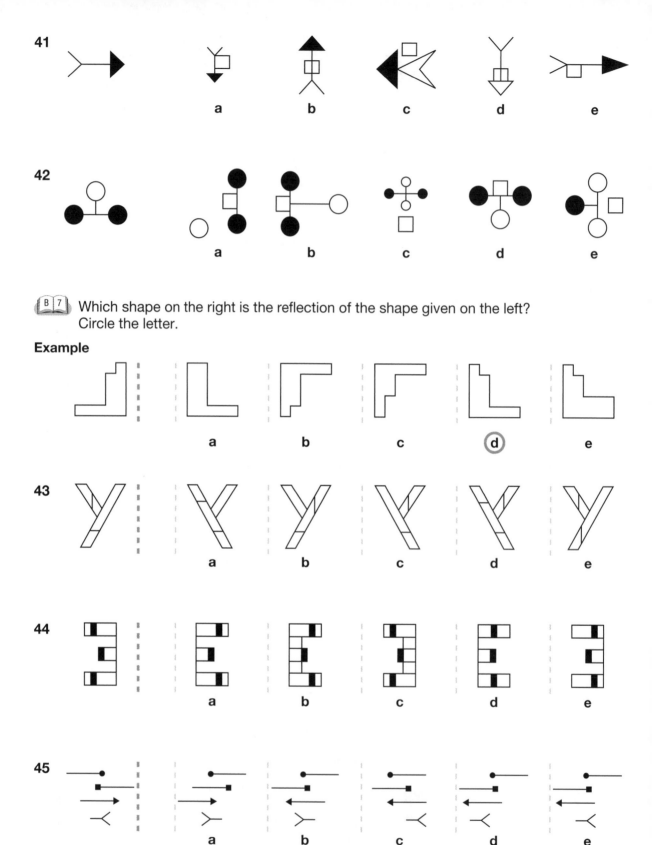

a   b   c   d   e

42

a   b   c   d   e

B 7 Which shape on the right is the reflection of the shape given on the left? Circle the letter.

Example

a   b   c   (d)   e

43

a   b   c   d   e

44

a   b   c   d   e

45

a   b   c   d   e

46

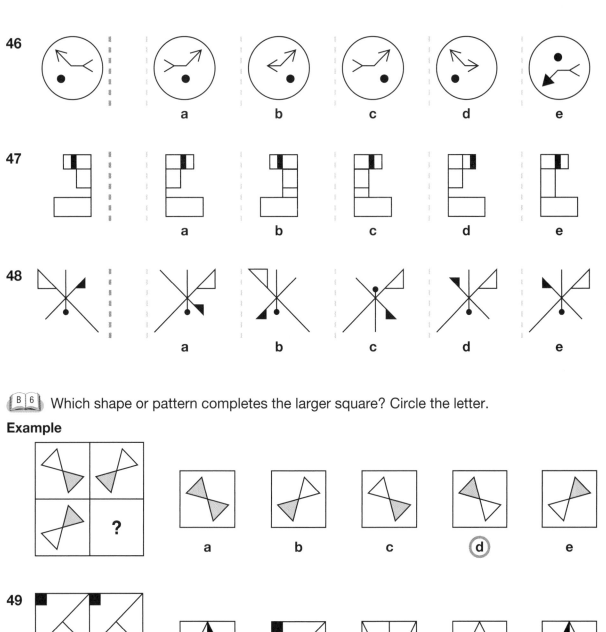

47

48

B 6 Which shape or pattern completes the larger square? Circle the letter.

Example

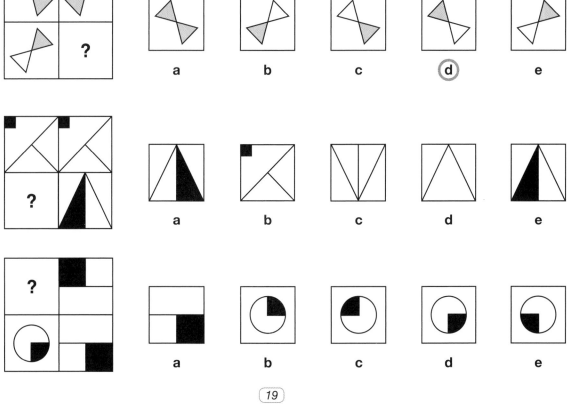

49

50

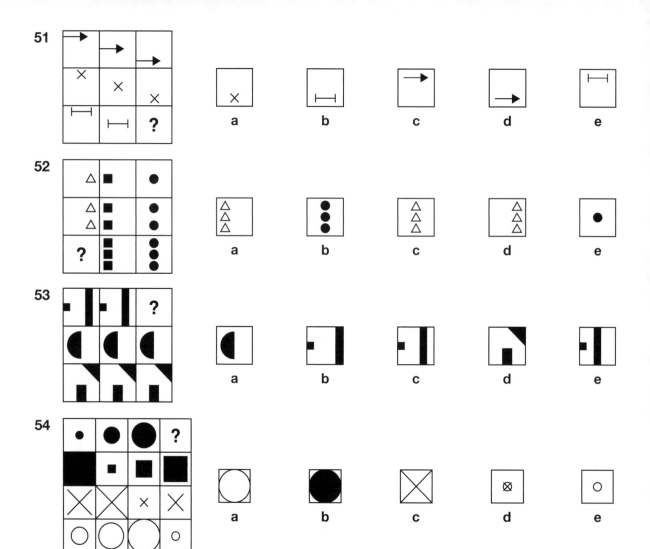

51

a   b   c   d   e

52

a   b   c   d   e

53

a   b   c   d   e

54

a   b   c   d   e

Paper 3

Which is the odd one out? Circle the letter.

Example

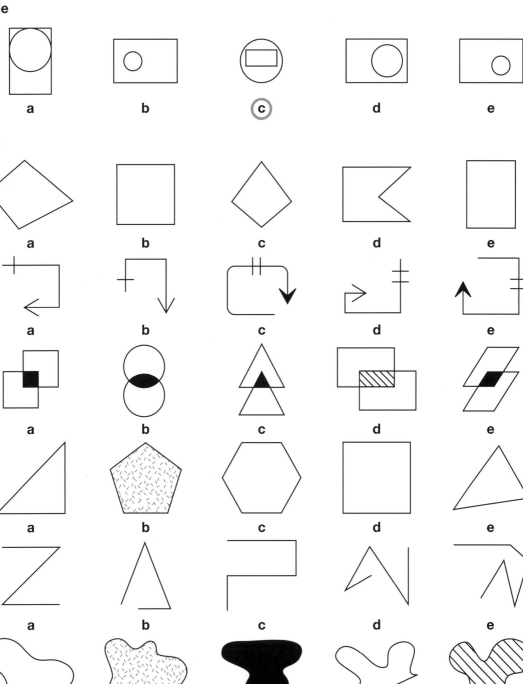

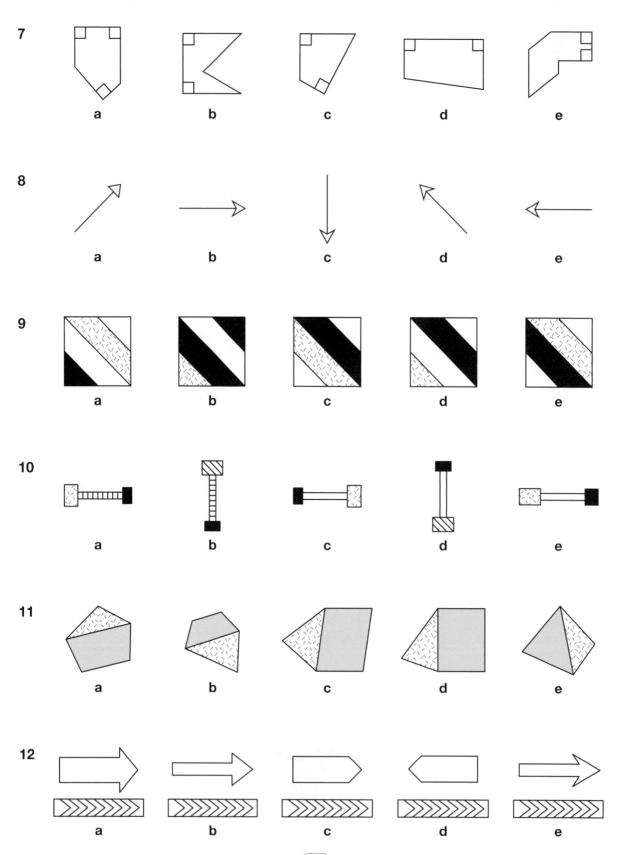

7
    a   b   c   d   e

8
    a   b   c   d   e

9
    a   b   c   d   e

10
    a   b   c   d   e

11
    a   b   c   d   e

12
    a   b   c   d   e

Which one comes next? Circle the letter.

Example

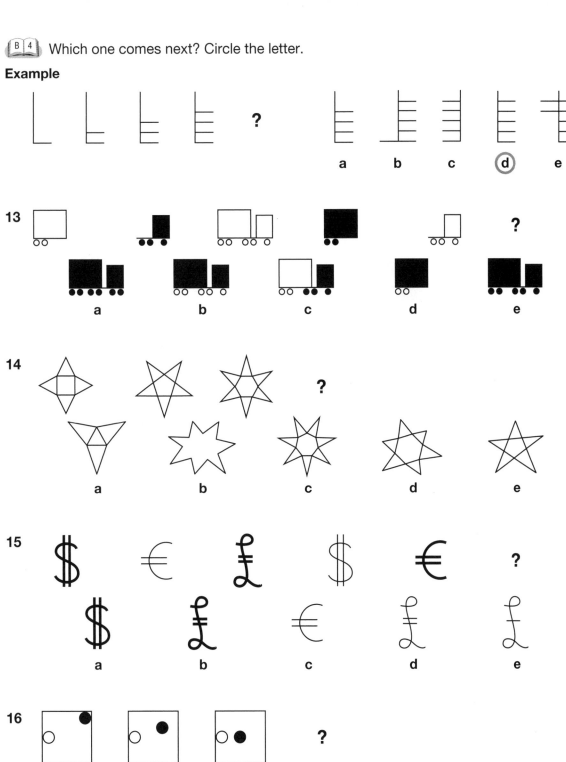

13

14

15

16

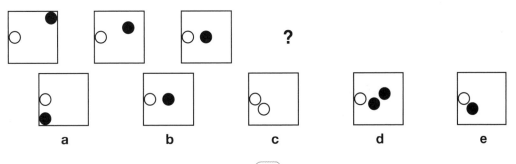

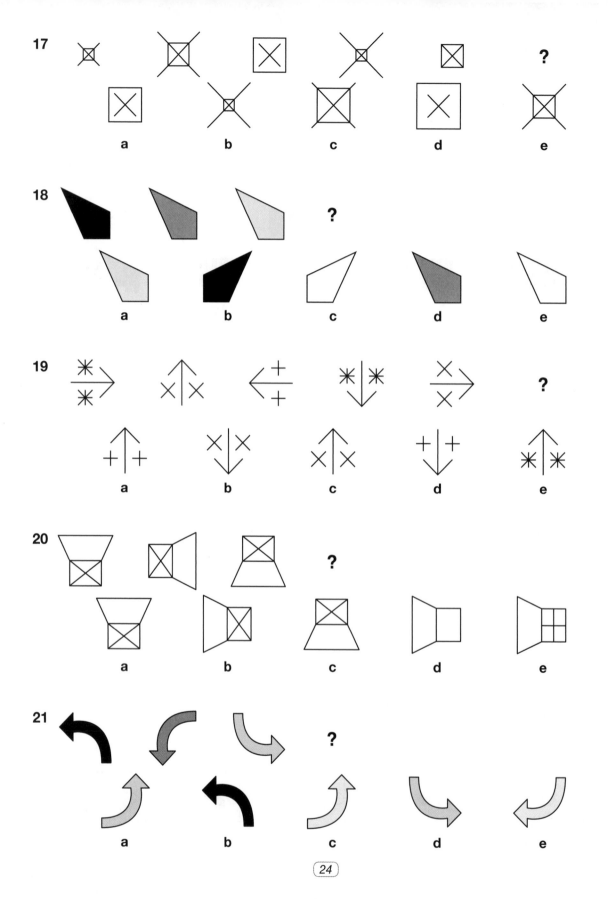

22

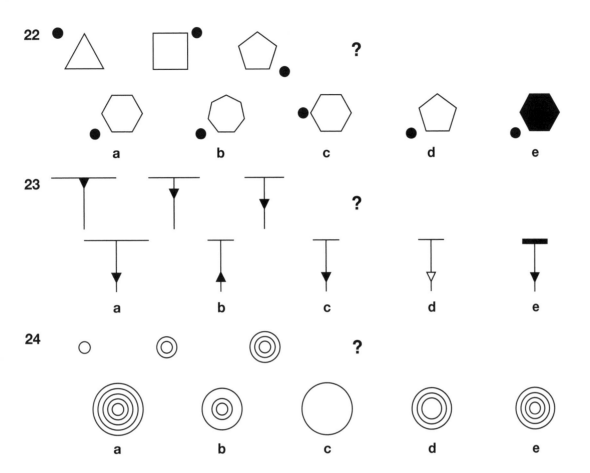

a   b   c   d   e

23

a   b   c   d   e

24

a   b   c   d   e

 B 3 Which shape or pattern on the right completes the second pair in the same way as the first pair? Circle the letter.

Example

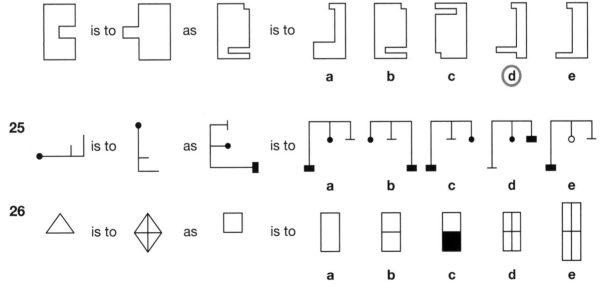

a   b   c   d   e

25

a   b   c   d   e

26

a   b   c   d   e

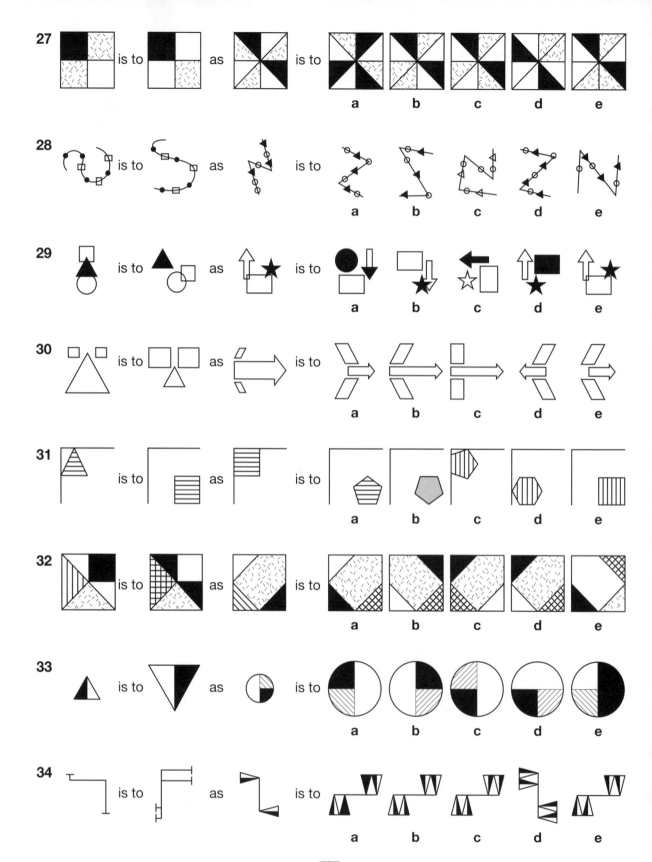

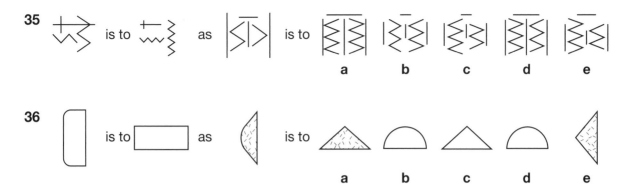

35

a   b   c   d   e

36

a   b   c   d   e

B 6   Which shape or pattern completes the larger square? Circle the letter.

Example

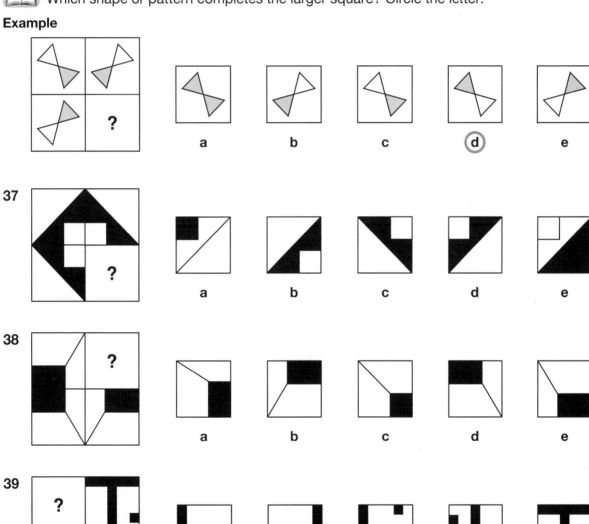

a   b   c   (d)   e

37

a   b   c   d   e

38

a   b   c   d   e

39

a   b   c   d   e

40

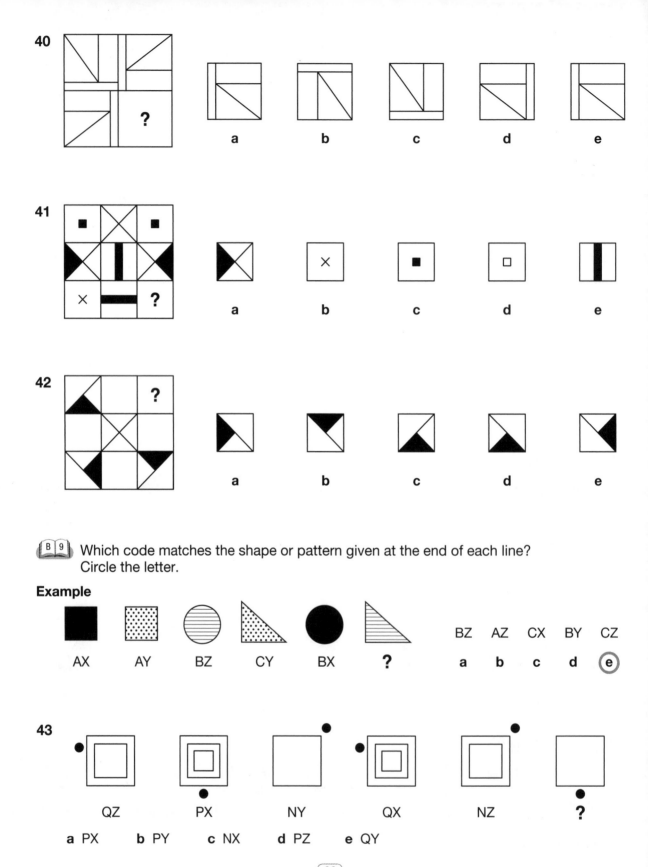

a b c d e

41

a b c d e

42

a b c d e

Which code matches the shape or pattern given at the end of each line?
Circle the letter.

Example

AX AY BZ CY BX ?

BZ AZ CX BY CZ
a b c d **e**

43

QZ PX NY QX NZ ?

a PX **b** PY **c** NX **d** PZ **e** QY

28

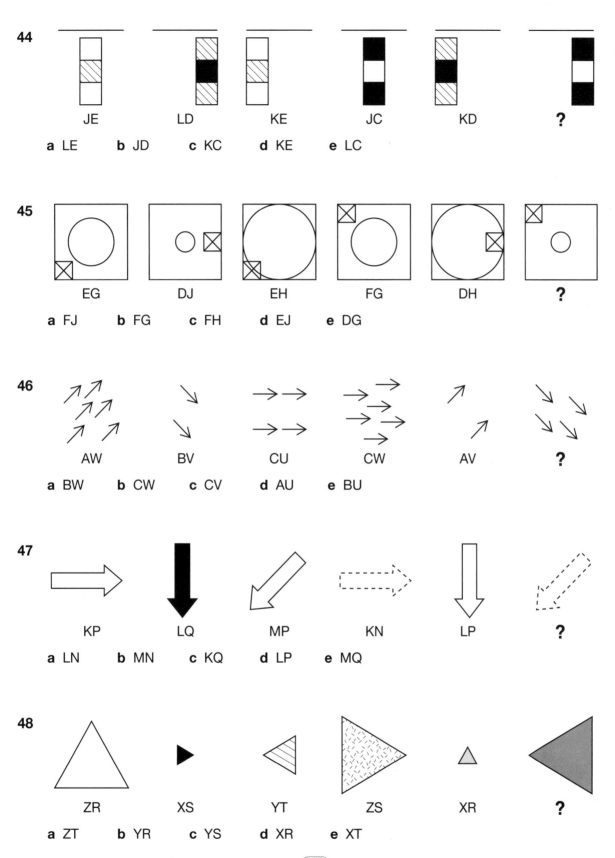

44

JE LD KE JC KD **?**

a LE   b JD   c KC   d KE   e LC

45

EG DJ EH FG DH **?**

a FJ   b FG   c FH   d EJ   e DG

46

AW BV CU CW AV **?**

a BW   b CW   c CV   d AU   e BU

47

KP LQ MP KN LP **?**

a LN   b MN   c KQ   d LP   e MQ

48

ZR XS YT ZS XR **?**

a ZT   b YR   c YS   d XR   e XT

Which shape or pattern is made when the first two shapes or patterns are put together? Circle the letter.

Example

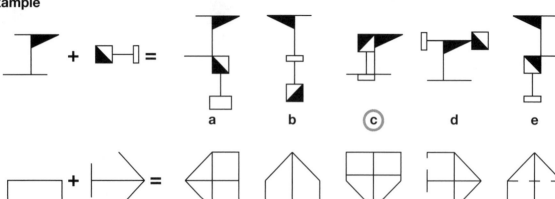

49

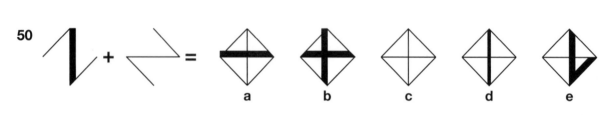

50

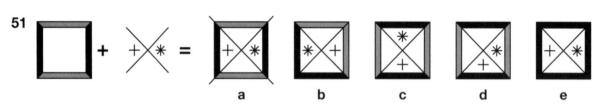

51

52

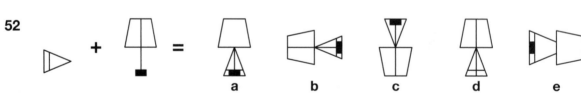

53

54

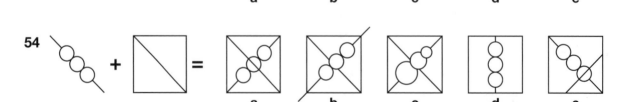

1 **d** All of the shapes, apart from d, are rectangles.
2 **e** All of the options, apart from e, consist of a square and a triangle which are not touching.
3 **d** All of the shapes, apart from d, are triangles with three acute angles.
4 **a** All of the options, apart from a, consist of a long line with a number of shorter lines which are all at 90° to the long line.
5 **e** All of the options, apart from e, consist of two rectangle that touch at a corner.
6 **e** All of the shapes, apart from e, are ovals.
7 **c** All of the options, apart from c, consist of a circle inside of a rectangle.
8 **a** All of the shapes, apart from a, are right-angled triangles.
9 **d** All of the options, apart from d, consist of a number of lines which are all at 90° to each other.
10 **b** All of the options, apart from b, consist of a triangle and a square which are not touching each other.
11 **b** All of the shapes, apart from b, include an arrow pointing up to the right.
12 **a** All of the options, apart from a, include a curved arrow pointing anti-clockwise.
13 **d** This is a repeating pattern: white square, white right-angled triangle, light grey right-angled triangle, dark grey square.
14 **b** The number of lines continues to increase. Each new line is at 45° to the previous line.
15 **b** The number of white sections continues to increase. The sections of the circle stay in the same place.
16 **d** A small black triangle is added to each corner of the square in turn. In the last picture of the sequence, the triangle has been added to a previous triangle to form a square.
17 **b** The height of the parallelogram continues to decrease.
18 **c** This is a repeating pattern with four shapes. The second and sixth picture are the same, therefore the third and seventh picture will also be the same.
19 **a** The arrow continues to rotate by 45° clockwise.
20 **c** This is a repeating pattern with four shapes. The second and sixth picture are the same, therefore the third and seventh picture will also be the same.
21 **b** The small square alternates between black and white. There is only one line inside the rectangle.
22 **e** The shape continues to rotate by 45° clockwise.

23 **a** This is a repeating pattern with four shapes. The second and sixth picture are the same, therefore the third and seventh picture will also be the same.
24 **b** The number of black circles continues to decrease. The black circles are on a curved line.
25 **b** The second shape is a 90° clockwise rotation of the first shape.
26 **c** The second shape is a horizontal reflection of the first shape, with the central horizontal line removed.
27 **c** The second shape has the same pattern as the first shape.
28 **d** The second shape is the first shape with the smaller shapes at the end of the lines removed.
29 **b** The second pattern consists of the same shapes as the first pattern, with their positions swapped.
30 **d** The second shape is the first shape with its width and height doubled.
31 **d** The second shape is the first shape with missing corner added, and rotated 90° clockwise.
32 **e** The same number of small shapes have been stacked vertically in the second shape, without overlapping.
33 **e** The second line is the first line rotated 90° clockwise and is dashed rather than solid.
34 **a** The second shape is a vertical reflection of the first shape. In the second shape, the striped area has become grey and the white area has become black.
35 **c** The second pattern consists of the first shape, plus the first shape rotated 90°, 180° and 270°.
36 **a** The second pattern consists of the shapes in the first pattern joined together and then rotated 90° anti-clockwise.

37 **a**
38 **c**
39 **d**
40 **e**

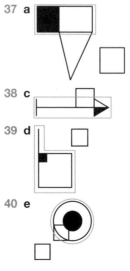

41 c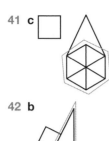

42 b

43–48 When each shape is paired with the correct reflection, they form a single shape that is perfectly symmetrical.

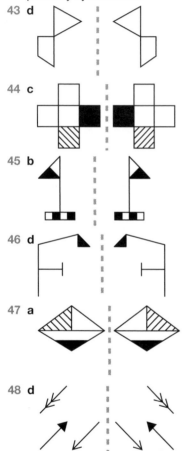

43 d

44 c

45 b

46 d

47 a

48 d

49 e The first letter represents the shape inside the flag (A has a star, B has a circle and C has a triangle). The second letter represents the position of the flag on the stem (D has the flag in the middle, E has the flag at the top and F has the flag at the bottom).

50 b The first letter represents the shapes used in the pattern (K has triangles, L has squares and M has circles). The second represents the direction in which the shapes are arranged (G has the shapes arranged horizontally, H has the shapes arranged vertically and J has the shape arranged diagonally).

51 c The first letter represents the number of vertical lines inside the rectangle (P has two lines, Q has one line and N has three lines). The second letter represents the shape on top of the rectangle (R has a semicircle, S has a triangle and T has a trapezium).

52 d The first letter represents the shape (X has an inverted L-shape, Y has a cross shape and Z has a rotated T-shape). The second letter represents the colour of the shape (U has a grey fill, V has a black fill and W has a white fill).

53 e The first letter represents the shape (K has a bow-tie shape, L has a rotated capital I and M has an arrow). The second letter represents the shape's size (A has a large shape, B has a small shape and C has a medium shape).

54 d The first letter represents the position of the arrows (G has the arrows at the bottom, H has the arrows at the top and J has the arrows in the middle). The second letter represents the direction in which the arrows are pointing (R has arrows pointing up to the right, S has arrows pointing up to the left and T has arrows pointing straight up).

1 **a** All of the shapes, apart from a, consist of two curved lines.
2 **e** All of the shapes, apart from e, have shading with short lines.
3 **b** All of the patterns, apart from b, consist of a triangle, a circle and two rectangles.
4 **b** All of the arrows, apart from b, have a large arrowhead.
5 **a** All of the options, apart from a, have the same pattern in both shapes.
6 **e** All of the arrows, apart from e, have three lines through the shaft.
7 **d** All of the shapes, apart from d, have a white triangle at the end.
8 **c** All of the squares, apart from c, have three lines inside them.
9 **b** All of the shapes, apart from b, are the same size.
10 **d** All of the patterns, apart from d, have a black circle.
11 **d** All of the patterns, apart from d, have small squares.
12 **a** All of the patterns, apart from a, have small squares.
13 **b** The two lines within the square continue to rotate by 45° anti-clockwise inside the square.
14 **b** The outer squares continue to be removed one at a time. The inner square alternates between black and white.
15 **e** The number of points on the star continues to decrease. All of the shapes are white and do not have anything inside them.
16 **a** The shapes alternate between circles and squares. There is a repeating pattern in the colour: all white, black inner shape with a white outer shape, white inner shape with a black outer shape.
17 **b** The black squares on the left continue to move downwards at the same distance each time.
18 **b** Alternate patterns have an outer square. The symbols follows a repeating pattern: +, ×, ÷.
19 **a** The number of circles in each 'arm' of the arrow shape continues to increase by two each time.
20 **e** The shape at the bottom alternates between a circle and a square, with the first two black, the next two white, the next two black and so on. At the top is a repeating pattern with three shapes.
21 **e** The square with the black triangle alternates between top-right and bottom-left. The other square follows a repeating pattern: white circle, black circle, no circle.
22 **d** The square continues to get darker.

23 **b** The trapezium at the top alternates between all white and white with a black triangle. The number of lines in the rectangle at the bottom follows a repeating pattern: one line, two lines, three lines.
24 **e** The circle continues to increase in size, with the same pattern.
25 **d** The second shape is vertical reflection of the first.
26 **d** The second shape is the first shape stretched vertically, with the white and black parts staying in the same position. The size of the second shape will increase by the same amount.
27 **e** The second shape is the same as the first shape with the colours reversed.
28 **c** The first pattern is the same as the first pattern with the bottom shape removed.
29 **e** The second pattern is the same as the first shape with the inner shape moved outside of the larger shape.
30 **b** The second pattern is the same as the first shape with both shapes made smaller.
31 **c** A diagonal reflection of the outer shape in the first pattern has been added. The shape inside the first triangle changes from white to black, so in the second pair this will change from black to white. The small shape inside the reflection will be the opposite colour.
32 **a** The first pattern is the second pattern with the arrow rotated 180° and moved to above the larger shape.
33 **b** The second pattern is the first pattern rotated 90° clockwise, with an extra copy of the shape at each end.
34 **c** The second shape is the first shape vertically reflected and halved in size.
35 **c** The second shape is the first shape rotated 90° anti-clockwise and doubled in size.
36 **a** The second shape is the first shape with each line widened into a hollow shape. The arrow-head changes from black to white.
37 **c**
38 **a**

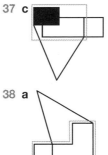

EXPANDED ANSWERS

Bond Non-Verbal Reasoning Assessment Papers 9–10 years Book 1

39 **e**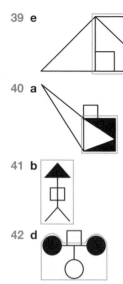

40 **a**

41 **b**

42 **d**

43–48 When each shape is paired with the correct reflection, they form a single shape that is perfectly symmetrical.

43 **c**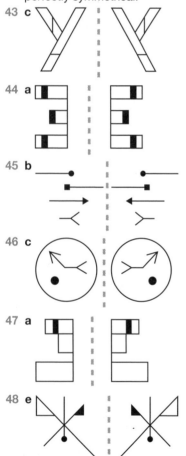

44 **a**

45 **b**

46 **c**

47 **a**

48 **e**

49 **e** The missing shape will be the same as the bottom right square.

50 **c** The missing square will be a 180° rotation of the bottom left square.

51 **b** In each row, from left to right, the shape moves down slightly. The first row has an arrow; the second row has a cross; and the third row has a capital 'I' shape on its side. This means the missing square will have a capital 'I' shape on its side at the bottom of the square.

52 **d** The top row has 1 shape in each square; the second row has 2 shapes in each square; the third row has 3 shapes in each square. The first column has white triangles; the second column has black squares; the third column has black circles. The shapes in each column are in the same position. This means the missing square will have 3 white triangles to the right of the square.

53 **c** Each row shows a shape that is repeated in the next square. The missing square will be the same as the other shapes in the top row.

54 **b** Each row has the same shape increasing in size, in a repeating pattern: small, medium, large, very large, small, medium, large, and so on. This means the shape in the missing square will be very large black circle.

1 **d** All of the shapes, apart from d, are quadrilaterals.
2 **c** All of the shapes, apart from c, are arrows made from straight lines.
3 **d** All of the patterns, apart from d, have an intersection that is coloured black.
4 **b** All of the shapes, apart from b, are white.
5 **c** All of the patterns, apart from c, are made from lines that meet at non-right angles.
6 **d** All of the shapes, apart from d, have curved outlines with no straight lines.
7 **a** All of the shapes, apart from a, have two right angles.
8 **a** All of the arrows, apart from a, have an arrowhead that is a quadrilateral.
9 **b** All of the shapes, apart from b, have one black section and two white sections.
10 **e** All of the patterns, apart from e, have an identical small black rectangle at one end of the central rectangle, and a larger rectangle at the other end with its longer side at right angles to the central rectangle.
11 **e** All of the patterns, apart from e, have a grey quadrilateral.
12 **d** All of the shapes, apart from e, have an arrow pointing to the right.
13 **e** This is a repeating pattern with three shapes. The shapes alternate between black and white.
14 **c** The number of points on the star continues to increase. There is a polygon at the centre of the star.
15 **d** This is a repeating pattern with three symbols. The symbols alternate between bold and not bold.
16 **e** The black circle continues to move across the square, from top right to bottom left.
17 **c** The size of the square follows a repeating pattern: small, medium, large. The size of the cross alternates between small and large.
18 **e** The kite continues to get lighter.
19 **a** The arrow continues to rotate 90° anti-clockwise. The shapes on either side of the shaft of the arrow follow a repeating pattern: star, cross, plus.
20 **b** The shape continues to rotate 90° clockwise.
21 **c** The arrow continues to rotate 90° anti-clockwise, and continues to get lighter.
22 **a** The number of lines that made up the large shape continues to increase by one each time. The black circle continues to move clockwise around the shape.
23 **c** The arrowhead continues to move down the vertical line, and the horizontal line continues to get shorter.

24 **e** The number of circles continue to increase by one each time.
25 **a** The second shape is a 90° clockwise rotation of the first shape.
26 **d** The second shape is made by horizontally reflecting the first shape and adding a vertical line through the middle.
27 **c** The second shape is the same as the first shape, with the white sections turning speckled and the speckled sections turning white.
28 **a** The second shape has the same number of white shapes and the same number of black shapes as the first.
29 **b** The second pattern has the same shapes as the first pattern. In the second pattern, two of the shapes overlap and the other is separate.
30 **e** The second pattern is the same as the first pattern, with the small shapes made larger and the large shapes made smaller.
31 **a** The second pattern has a shape with one more side than the shape in the first pattern. The shape has moved from the top left to the bottom right.
32 **c** The second pattern is the same as the first, but the black sections have become white, the white sections have become black and the striped section have become cross-hatched.
33 **a** The second shape is the first shape rotated 180° and enlarged.
34 **c** The second shape is two copies of the first shape, both rotated by 90° anti-clockwise and placed on top of each other.
35 **c** All of the vertical and horizontal lines in the second shape have been made smaller. The zig-zags have been reflected horizontally.
36 **a** The second shape is a 90° clockwise rotation of the first shape, with the rounded corners made pointed.
37 **d** The missing square will be a vertical reflection of the bottom left square.
38 **e** The missing square will be a vertical reflection of the top left square.
39 **c** The missing square will be a 90° clockwise rotation of the bottom left square.
40 **b** The missing square will be a 90° clockwise rotation of the top right square.
41 **b** The whole grid has a line of symmetry running down the middle, so the missing square will be a vertical reflection of the bottom left square.
42 **a** The missing square will be a 90° clockwise rotation of the top left square.
43 **b** The first letter represents the position of the black circle (P has the circle at the bottom, Q has the circle on the left near the top and

EXPANDED ANSWERS

Bond Non-Verbal Reasoning Assessment Papers 9–10 years Book 1

N has the circle at the top right). The second letter represents the number of squares (X has three squares, Y has one square and Z has two squares).

44 **e** The first letter represents the position of the three squares (J has the squares at the centre of the horizontal line, K has the squares on the left and L has the squares on the right). The second letter represents the pattern of the squares (C has black squares top and bottom and a white square in the middle, D has diagonally striped squares top and bottom and a black square in the middle, and E has white squares top and bottom and a diagonally striped square in the middle).

45 **a** The first letter represents the position of the smaller square (D has the square middle right, E has the square bottom-left and F has the square top left). The second letter represents the size of the circle (G has a medium circle, H has a large circle and J has a small circle).

46 **e** The first letter represents the direction of the arrows (A has arrows pointing up and to the right, B has arrows pointing down and to the right and C has arrows pointing right). The second letter represents the number of arrows (U has four arrows, V has two arrows and W has six arrows).

47 **b** The first letter represents the direction of the arrow (K has the arrow pointing right, L has the arrow pointing down and M has the arrow pointing down and to the left). The second letter represents the pattern of the arrow (P has a white arrow with a solid line, Q has a black arrow and N has a white arrow with a dashed line).

48 **a** The first letter represents the size of the triangle (X has a small triangle, Y has a medium triangle and Z has a large triangle). The second letter represents the direction the triangle points in (R has a triangle pointing up, S has a triangle pointing right and T has a triangle pointing left).

49 **a**

The first shape has been rotated 90° anti-clockwise. The second shape has been rotated 180°.

50 **a**

The first shape has been rotated 90° anti-clockwise. The second shape has been rotated 90° clockwise.

51 **c**

The first shape has been rotated 90°. The second shape has been rotated 90° anti-clockwise.

52 **b**

The first shape has been rotated 180°. The second shape has been rotated 90° anti-clockwise.

53 **d**

Placing the shapes up against each other creates three rectangles on the left and one rectangle on the right.

54 **a**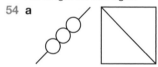

The first picture has been rotated 90°.

1 **c** All of the circles, apart from c, have a line that passes all the way through it.
2 **c** All of the patterns, apart from c, consist of three copies of a small shape.
3 **b** All of the patterns, apart from b, consist of two shapes of the same size.
4 **d** All of the patterns, apart from d, include the same sized cross.
5 **c** All of the patterns, apart from c, consist of six copies of a small shape.
6 **a** All of the patterns, apart from a, have circle at the corner of the triangle.
7 **e** All of the patterns, apart from e, have five horizontal lines.
8 **a** All of the patterns, apart from a, have a small shape completely inside the square.
9 **c** All of the patterns, apart from c, include a small black circle.
10 **d** All of the patterns, apart from d, have a white circle inside a larger shape.
11 **e** All of the shapes, apart from e, have a straight line through a sharp corner in the main shape.
12 **d** All of the patterns, apart from d, include a plus shape (+).
13 **d** This is a repeating pattern with four shapes.
14 **a** The black circle continues to move clockwise, from corner to corner, around the square. The arrow continues to move anti-clockwise around the square.
15 **d** This is a repeating pattern with three shapes. The shading of the shapes alternates between white and speckled.
16 **b** The arrow continues to rotate 45° anti-clockwise.
17 **d** The top shape follows a repeating pattern with four shapes. Within the repeating pattern, the number of lines making the shape decreases by one each time. The bottom shape alternates between a circle and a square.
18 **a** The arrowhead continues to get smaller.
19 **e** The sun follows a repeating pattern: just a circle, circle with rays, no sun. The size of the house follows a repeating pattern: large, medium, small. The roof alternates between a trapezium and a triangle. Alternate houses have a door.
20 **e** A shape continues to be added each time. The existing shapes do not change or move.
21 **e** The white band continues to move to the left.
22 **b** This white square continues to move anti-clockwise inside the main square. The main square has an extra black quarter each time.

23 **e** The number of sides making up the shape continues to decrease. The lines of all the shapes are the same length, so the shapes appear to get smaller.
24 **b** The arrow continues to rotate 45° clockwise. An extra pair of lines continue to be added to the end of the arrow each time.
25 **d** The second shape is a 90° anti-clockwise rotation of the first shape.
26 **a** The second pattern has the same shapes as the first pattern, but the circles have become grey and the squares have become black.
27 **d** The second pattern has one more flower than the first pattern. The flowers in the second pattern have one fewer petal each than the flowers in the first pattern.
28 **c** The second shape is the same as the first shape, but the second line from the centre becomes dashed and the third line from the centre becomes solid. The second shape needs to be an isosceles triangle, like the first shape, therefore it cannot be a.
29 **b** The second shape is the same as the first shape, with the shorter lines reflected diagonally on the large line.
30 **c** The second pattern consists of the same main shape as in the first pattern. An extra shape has been added to the three smaller shapes, which are then arranged outside the main shape as if at the four corners of a square. The pattern in the shape remains the same.
31 **a** The second pattern is a vertical reflection of the first pattern. The black small shapes become white and the white small shapes become black.
32 **d** The second pattern consists of two copies of the first pattern side by side, with the curved lines made straight.
33 **d** The second pattern is a 90° anti-clockwise rotation of the first pattern. The striped sections have become black and the speckled sections have become white.
34 **a** In the second pattern, the bottom-right shape has been vertically reflected along it's left-hand side.
35 **c** The second shape formation is the same as the first one, with the small vertical line attached to the upper shape removed. The white areas have become grey and the striped sections have become black.
36 **c** The second shape is a 90° clockwise rotation of the first shape, halved in size.

Bond Non-Verbal Reasoning Assessment Papers 9–10 years Book 1

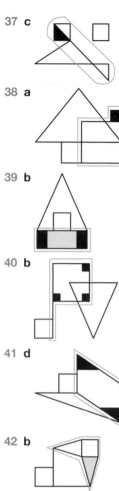

37 c

38 a

39 b

40 b

41 d

42 b

44 **e** The first row has 1 shape or line; the second row has 2 shapes or lines; and the third row has 3. The first column has arrows; the second column has diagonal lines; and the third column has lines with a black dot at the end. This means the missing square will have 1 line with a black dot at the end.

45 **d** The missing square will have a white arrow, the same as the others in the third column.

46 **e** The missing square will have the same shape as the others in the first column.

47 **e** Each row shows a different type of shape: the first row has crosses; the second row has black dots; the third row has black squares; and the fourth row has white triangles. The first column has 4 shapes, the second column has 3, the third has 2 and the fourth has 1. This means the missing square will have 4 white triangles.

48 **d** The lines inside the squares follow a pattern of: 4 lines, 3 lines, 2 lines, 1 line, 4 lines, 3 lines, 2 lines, and so on, The pattern starts at different points in each row and column. The square above and the square to the left of the missing square each have 2 lines. This means the missing square will have 1 line.

49 **b** The two + symbols are in opposite positions, so they cannot therefore be seen as adjacent faces on the cube.

50 **b** The two circles are in opposite positions, so they cannot therefore be seen as adjacent faces on the cube.

51 **a** The bottom white square in the net and the cross are in opposite positions, so these two faces cannot therefore be seen as adjacent faces on the cube. The other two white squares are in opposite positions, so they also cannot be seen as adjacent faces on the cube.

52 **b** The large white square and the large white square with a cross inside it are in opposite positions, so they cannot therefore be seen as adjacent faces on the cube.

53 **c** If the circle with a cross forms the top face and the large white circle below it in the net forms the front face, the large black circle would form the right face.

54 **d** If the thin cross (×) forms the front face and the small plus sign forms the right face, the thick, black cross must form the top face.

1 **a** All of the shapes, apart from a, are pentagons.
2 **e** All of the shapes, apart from e, have a white central square.
3 **c** All of the arrows, apart from c, have the same size arrowhead.
4 **b** All of the shapes, apart from b, are the same size.
5 **c** All of the shapes, apart from c, have the same pattern in both sections.
6 **e** All of the shapes, apart from e, are pentagons with a line through.
7 **a** All of the patterns, apart from a, consist of a circle and a square, with different shading.
8 **d** All of the shapes, apart from d, are a segment of a circle.
9 **c** All of the squares, apart from c, are the same size.
10 **d** All of the patterns, apart from d, have an L-shape inside the square.
11 **c** All of the patterns, apart from c, include a triangle of the same size.
12 **a** All of the patterns, apart from a, have black shading in the intersection between the two shapes.
13 **e** This is a repeating pattern with four shapes. The second and sixth picture are the same, therefore the third and seventh picture will also be the same.
14 **c** The number of lines that make the shape continues to increase by one each time.
15 **b** The curved arrow continues to move anticlockwise around the pattern. The central circle alternates between a black dot and a white circle. The square at bottom left follows a repeating pattern: no square, small square, large square.
16 **a** The black square continues to move to the right.
17 **e** This is a repeating pattern with three shapes. The shading of the triangles alternates between striped and white.
18 **e** The number of circles continues to decrease. The number of stars remains the same.
19 **b** The colour of the shape alternates between black and white. The number of lines that made the shape continues to increase. The arrow changes direction before moving to a new position.
20 **b** The number of lines that make the arrow continues to increase by one each time.

21 **a** The black square continues to move in a diagonal direction from top right to bottom left. The circle continues to get smaller.
22 **c** The number of lines to make the shape continues to decrease by one each time. The shape continues to get lighter.
23 **b** The arrow continues to rotate 45° anti-clockwise, and continues to get lighter.
24 **e** The black strip continues to move to the right and the white rectangle moves further up each time.
25 **d** The second shape would complete the first shape to make a regular shape. The pattern needs to be the same.
26 **d** The second shape is an enlarged version of the first shape.
27 **c** The second shape is a vertical reflection of the first shape.
28 **b** The second shape is the same as the first shape, with the rectangles turned into ovals.
29 **d** The second pattern has three times as many squares and three times as many circles as the first pattern. The dark grey shapes have become white. The light grey shapes are placed either side of the new white shapes.
30 **e** The top part of the second pattern is a vertical reflection of the top part of the first pattern, however, the small lines at the end have moved further along the curved line. The bottom part of the second pattern is the same as in the first pattern.
31 **d** The second shape is a 90° clockwise rotation of the first shape, with its width doubled.
32 **a** The second pattern consists of two shapes, each with one more side than those in the first pattern.
33 **e** The second pattern is made from the lines in the first pattern, arranged to form a regular polygon, without touching.
34 **e** The outer shape becomes the inner shape and stays the same colour. The inner shape becomes the outer shape and stays the same colour.
35 **c** The second shape is the first shape made smaller, and the middle line has become dashed.
36 **a** The second shape is a vertical reflection of the first shape. The white sections have become black and the black sections have become white.
37–42 When each shape is paired with the correct reflection, they form a single shape that is perfectly symmetrical.

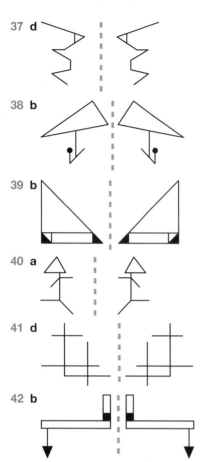

37 d

38 b

39 b

40 a

41 d

42 b

43 c The first letter represents the shapes (J has squares, K has triangles and L has rectangles). The second letter represents the number of shapes (F has three, G has two and H has four).

44 d The first letter represents the number of circles (D has one, E has five and F has three). The second letter represents the size of the circles (X has small circles, Y has large circles and Z has medium circles).

45 b The first letter represents the shape (P has a square, Q has a circle and N has a star). The second letter represents the shapes size (A has a large shape, B has a medium shape and C has a small shape).

46 c The first letter represents the colour of the arrow (K has a striped arrow, L has a white arrow and M has a black arrow). The second letter represents the direction in which the arrow points (U has an arrow pointing up to the left, V has an arrow pointing up to the right and W has an arrow pointing down to the right).

47 a The first letter represents the direction of the lines shaded in black (F has them pointing up, G has them pointing to the left and H has them pointing down). The second letter represents the number of layers in the shape (C has one layer, D has three layers and E has two layers).

48 c The first letter represents the pattern inside a section of the circle (K has a speckled section, L has a black section and M has a striped section). The second letter represents the size of the white section (X has one-quarter white, Y has three-quarters white and Z has half white).

49 b The small cross and the white circle are in opposite positions, therefore they cannot be seen as adjacent faces on the cube.

50 b The plus symbol and the white square are in opposite positions, therefore they cannot be seen as adjacent faces on the cube.

51 a The two white diamonds are in opposite positions, therefore they cannot be seen as adjacent faces on the cube.

52 e The black dot and the white face are in opposite positions, therefore they cannot be seen as adjacent faces on the cube.

53 b The black square and the plus symbol with lines inside it are in opposite positions, therefore they cannot be seen as adjacent faces on the cube.

54 c The white circle and the white face are in opposite positions, therefore they cannot be seen as adjacent faces on the cube.

1 **c** All of the patterns, apart from a, include a black circle.
2 **a** All of the arrows, apart from a, are pointing anti-clockwise.
3 **a** All of the patterns, apart from a, have three white shapes.
4 **e** All of the grids, apart from e, have four black squares.
5 **a** All of the triangles, apart from a, are right-angled triangles.
6 **c** All of the patterns, apart from c, have a black shape below a white shape.
7 **d** All of the patterns, apart from d, have two lines at right angles to each other.
8 **e** All of the flags, apart from e, are at the top of the flagpole.
9 **c** All of the patterns, apart from c, consist of lines that come together to make a triangle.
10 **b** All of the patterns, apart from b, have a square at the bottom of the vertical line and a circle at the top.
11 **d** All of the patterns, apart from d, have four lines coming out of different parts of the circle, and one black dot.
12 **e** All of the patterns, apart from e, include two straight lines forming a right angle, with three stars on one of the lines.
13 **b** This is a repeating pattern of four differently shaded shapes. The second and sixth picture are the same, therefore the third and seventh picture will also be the same.
14 **e** An additional section of the square continues to be shaded, alternating between black and speckled. The next square in a clockwise direction is shaded each time.
15 **d** The number of lines that make the shape continues to decrease by two each time.
16 **d** The square continues to increase in size.
17 **c** This is a repeating pattern with four shapes.
18 **b** The black square continues to move along the line.
19 **d** The number of shapes continues to increase. The number of sides that make the shapes continues to increase.
20 **e** The square continues to get larger and darker.
21 **d** The flag continues to move down the pole, and continues to point further downward.
22 **a** The black shape continues to move anti-clockwise around the cross. The number of sides that make the shape continue to decrease.
23 **e** This number of small squares within the large square continues to decrease.

24 **e** The arrow continues to rotate 90° clockwise. The tail of the arrow continues to move back towards the head.
25 **c** The second shape is a 135° anti-clockwise rotation of the first shape.
26 **a** The second pattern has half as many black shapes and half as many white shapes as the first pattern.
27 **d** In the second pattern, the C-shape has become a line and the white section has become black.
28 **b** The second pattern is the same as the first pattern, with the small shapes inside the left and middle squares swapped.
29 **b** The second shape is a vertical reflection of the first shape. The thick lines have become thin, and the thin lines have become thick.
30 **a** The second pattern is the two shapes from the first pattern joined together. The colours of the two shapes have been swapped.
31 **d** The second pattern is a vertical reflection of the first pattern, with the positions of the upper and lower shape swapped.
32 **b** The second pattern has twice as many crosses as the first pattern. Each cross is enclosed in a square.
33 **c** In the second pattern, the striped shape increases by one and changes to a speckled pattern. The white shapes have decreased by one and changed to black.
34 **d** The second pattern has one more line than the first pattern.
35 **b** The second pattern is the first pattern doubled in size. The white shapes have become black and the black shapes have become white.
36 **c** The second shape is a 90° clockwise rotation of the first shape. After the rotation, the small black shape at the top has been removed.
37 **a** The missing square will have a large shape, as in the top right square, and the shape will be a circle, as in the bottom left square.
38 **c** The missing square will be the top left square rotated 90° clockwise.
39 **b** Each row has a black circle, black square and black triangle. The lines in the whole grid are diagonally reflected. This means the missing square will have a circle with a white triangle in the bottom left corner.
40 **b** The whole grid has a line of symmetry running down the middle, so the missing square will be a vertical reflection of the bottom left square.
41 **a** The missing square will be a 90° clockwise rotation of the bottom left square.

Bond Non-Verbal Reasoning Assessment Papers 9–10 years Book 1

42 **e** The missing square will be a 90° clockwise rotation on the bottom right square.

43 **b** The first letter represents the pattern inside the shape (A has a speckled pattern, B has a white fill and C has stripes). The second letter represents the direction of the shape (G has the triangle pointing left, H has the triangle pointing down and J has the triangle pointing right).

44 **c** The first letter represents the number of small black triangles (D has three, E has one and F has two)The second letter represents the pattern of the large triangle (R has a large black triangle, S has a large white triangle and T has a large speckled triangle).

45 **c** The first letter represents the direction in which the arrowhead points (N has an arrowhead pointing right, P has an arrowhead pointing down and Q has an arrowhead pointing left). The second letter represents the size of the arrowhead (U has a small arrowhead, V has a medium arrowhead and W has a large arrowhead).

46 **a** The first letter represents the position of the black circle (D has the circle inside the square, E has the circle outside the square and F has the circle on the edge of the square). The second letter represents the pattern inside the square (K has a speckled pattern, L has stripes and M has a white fill).

47 **b** The first letter represents the direction of the U-shape (G has a U-shape with the open end down, H has the open end on the left and J has the open end up). The second letter represents the number of small lines on each side of the U-shape (U has three, V has four and W has one).

48 **a** The first letter represents the shape (S has an F-shape, T has an X-shape and U has a T-shape). The second represents the shape's size (W has a small shape, X has a medium shape and Y has a large shape).

49 **a**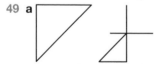

The large triangle has its right angle at the top left. The small triangle in the other shape has its right angle and bottom right. When they overlap, they create a new triangle.

50 **e**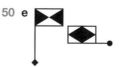

The first shape has black triangles left and right, and a small black square at the end of the line. The second shape has a large black diamond and a small black circle at the end of the line.

51 **d**

In both shapes the horizontal lines extend equally on both sides of the line and are evenly spaced. The bottom horizontal line in the first shape is the same length as the horizontal line in the second shape. Both vertical lines become one line when they overlap.

52 **a**

The first shape has a star under the right eye. The second shape has a dot under the left eye and zigzag hair. The semicircles in the first shape and the horizontal lines in the second shape combine to make open eyes.

53 **c**

The first shape has been rotated 90° clockwise. The second shape has three horizontal lines of different lengths across the vertical line. The black shapes form a new shape when overlapped.

54 **b**

The spiral spirals outwards in a clockwise direction. The second shape has a black triangle, with three horizontal lines of different lengths at the bottom of the vertical line, and four small black squares.

Paper 4

B 1   Which is the odd one out? Circle the letter.

Example

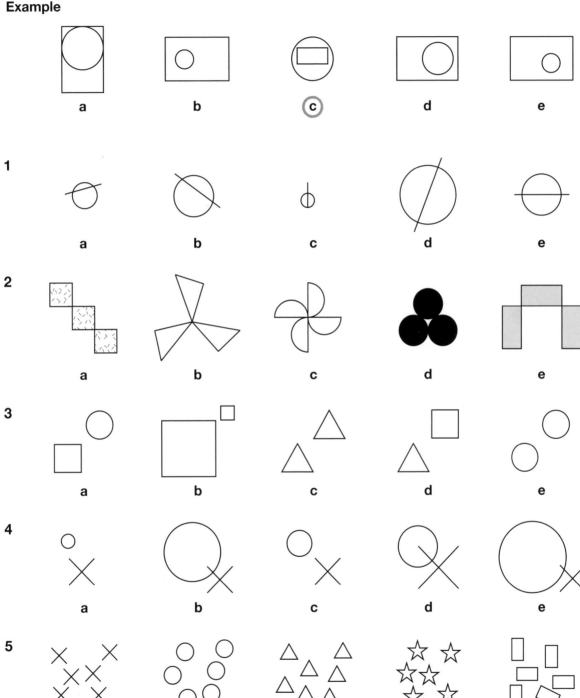

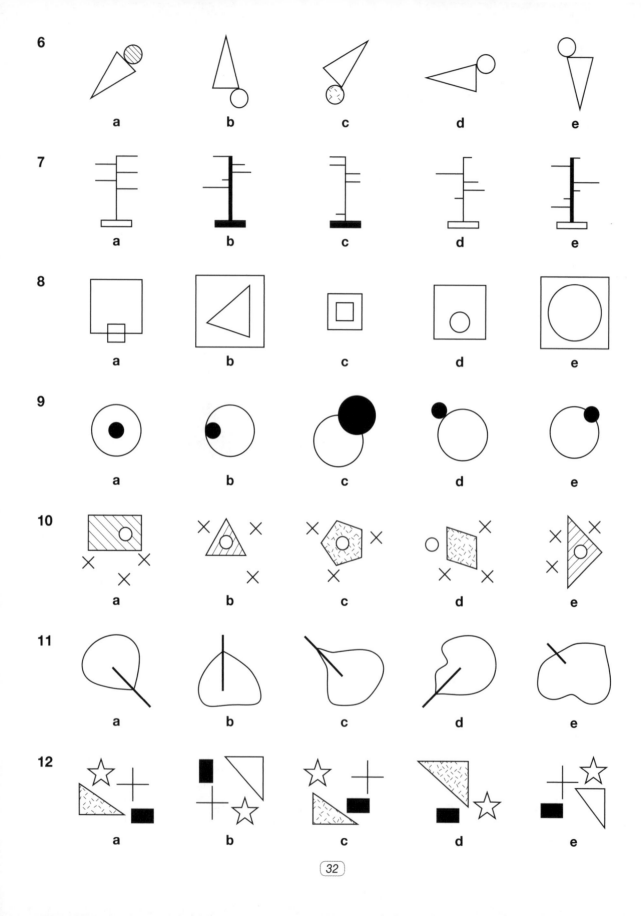

Which one comes next? Circle the letter.

Example

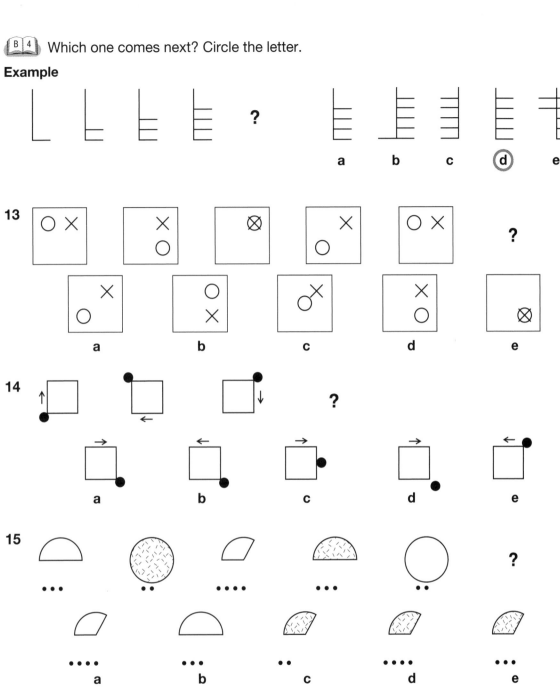

13

14

15

16

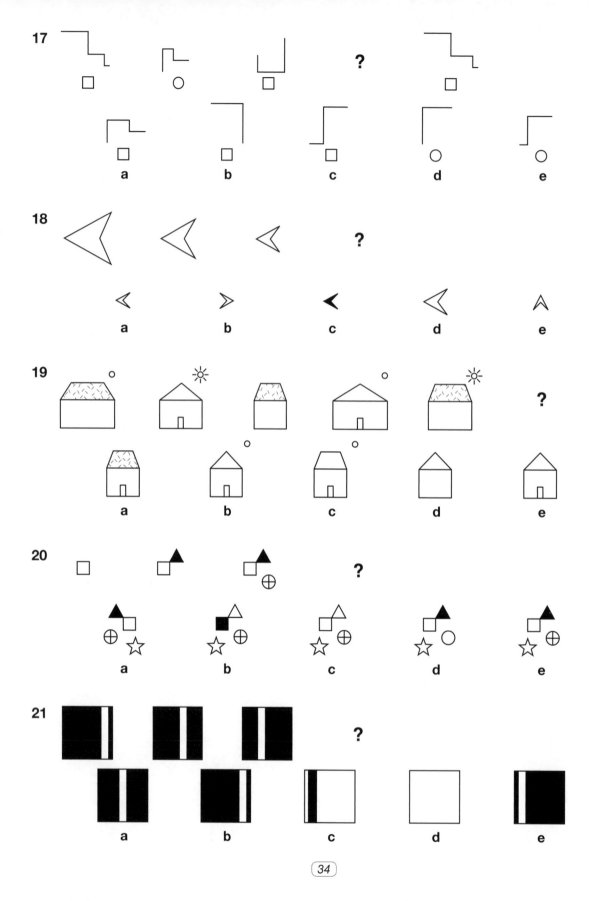

22

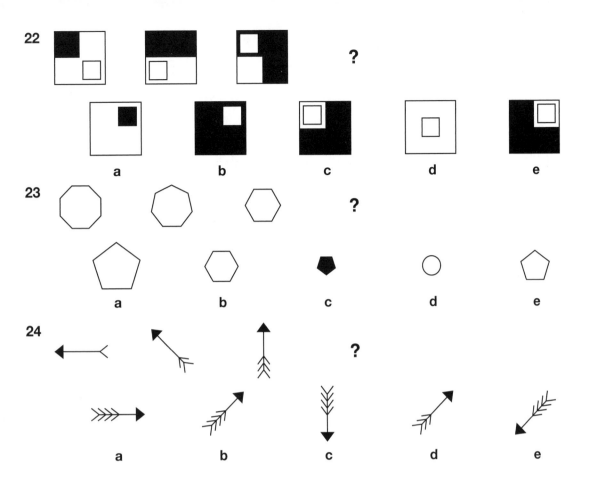

23

24

B 3 Which shape or pattern on the right completes the second pair in the same way as the first pair? Circle the letter.

Example

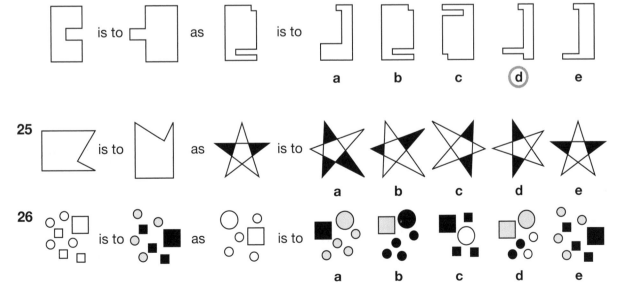

25

26

35

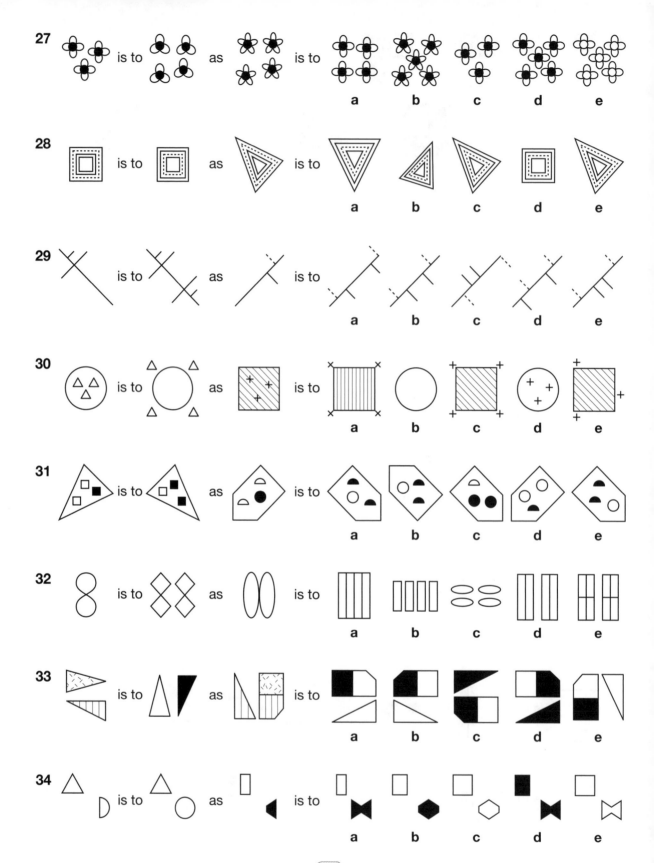

35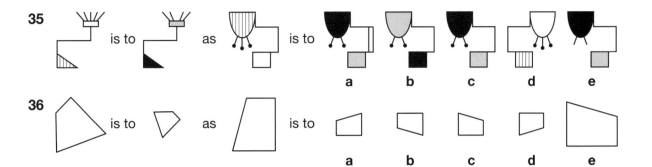

36

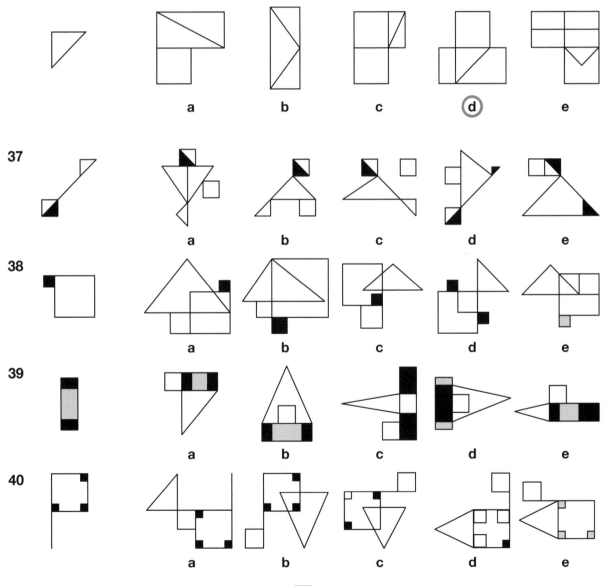

In which larger shape is the shape on the left hidden? Circle the letter.

Example

37

38

39

40

41

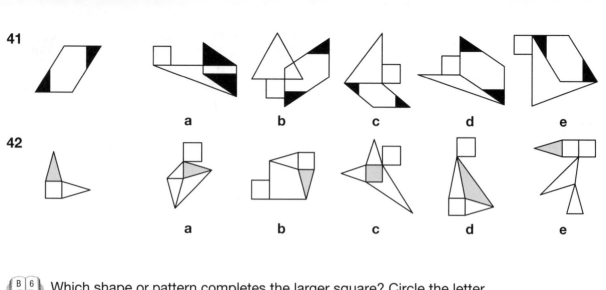

42

B 6 Which shape or pattern completes the larger square? Circle the letter.

Example

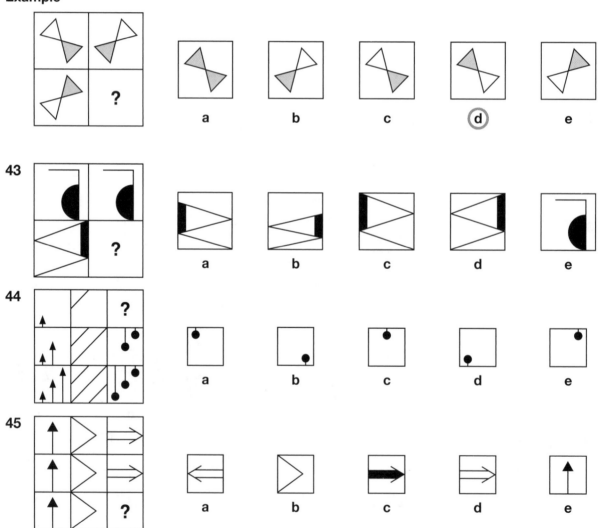

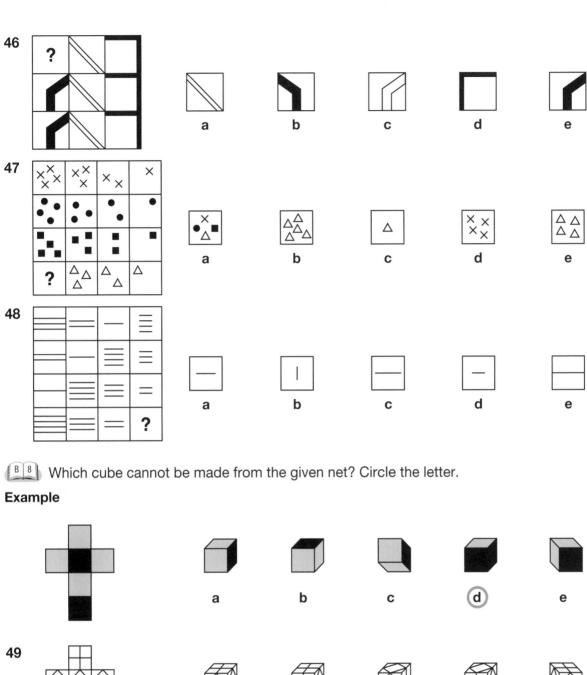

46

a   b   c   d   e

47

a   b   c   d   e

48

a   b   c   d   e

B 8   Which cube cannot be made from the given net? Circle the letter.

Example

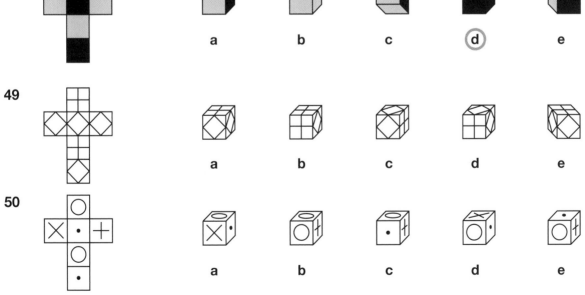

a   b   c   (d)   e

49

a   b   c   d   e

50

a   b   c   d   e

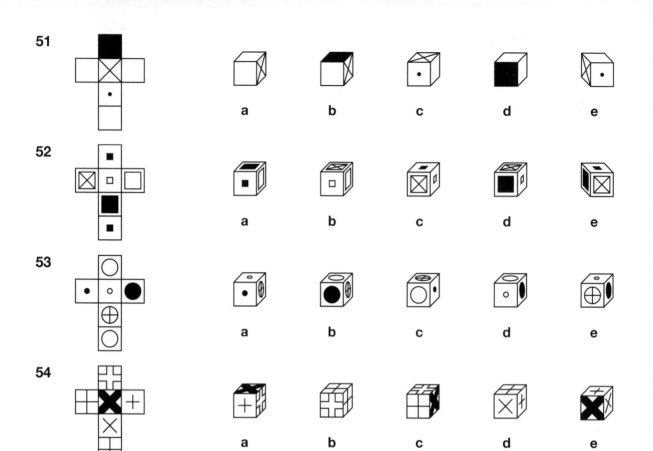

51

a   b   c   d   e

52

a   b   c   d   e

53

a   b   c   d   e

54

a   b   c   d   e

Now go to the Progress Chart to record your score!   Total   ◯   54

Paper 5

B 1 Which is the odd one out? Circle the letter.

Example

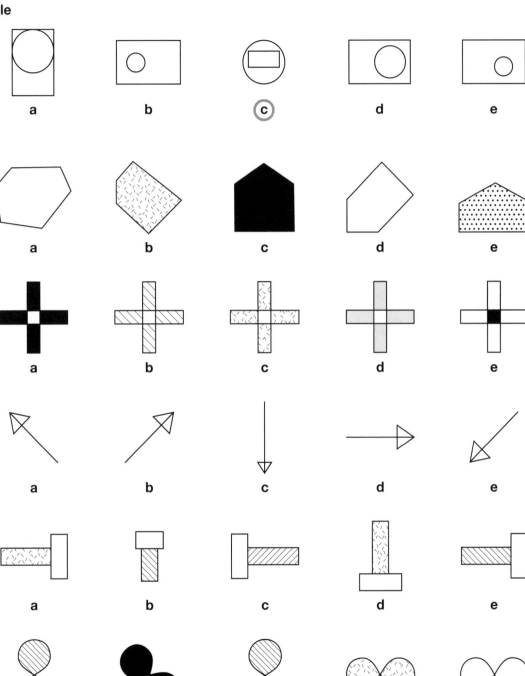

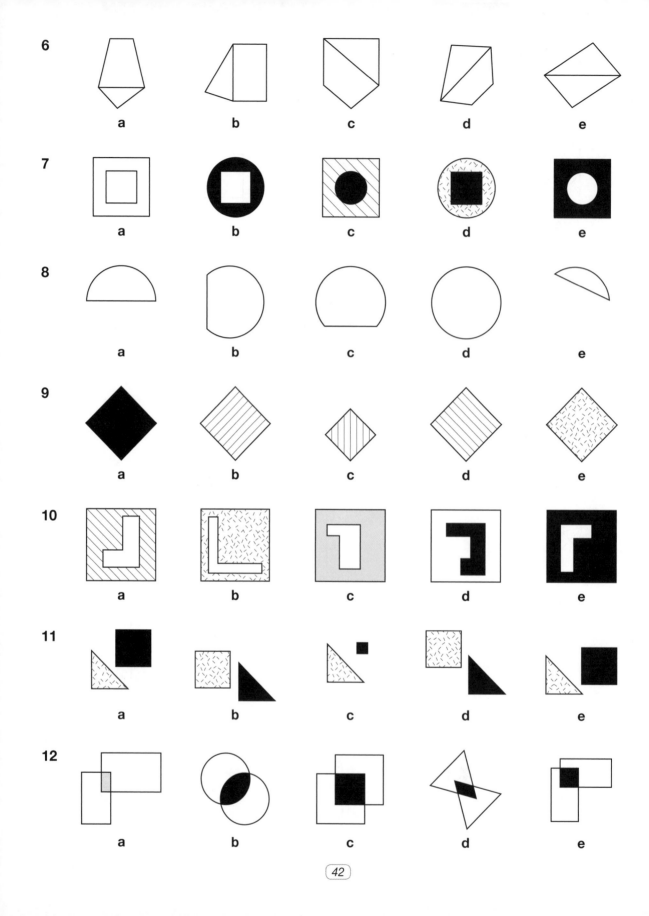

Which one comes next? Circle the letter.

Example

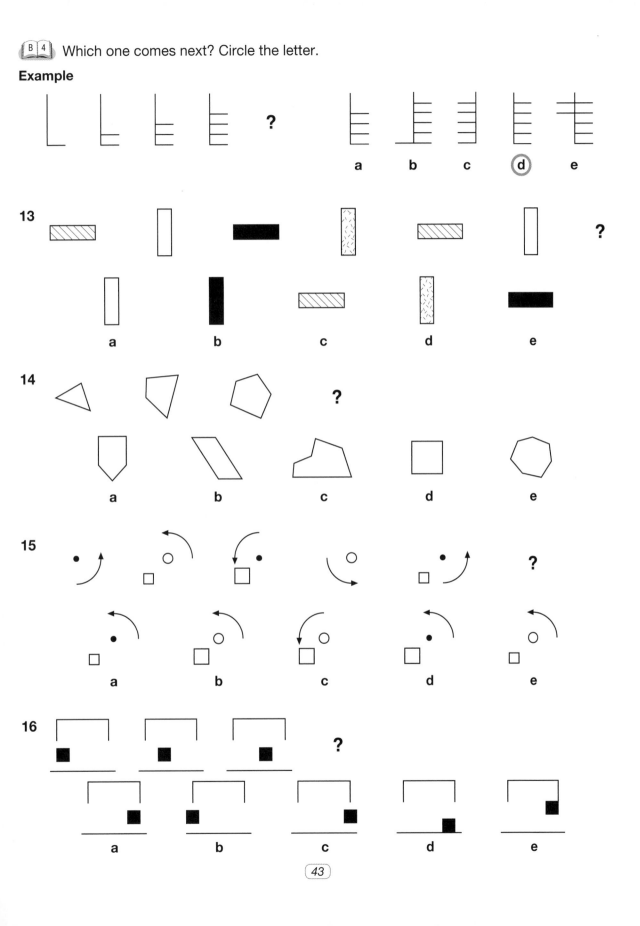

13

14

15

16

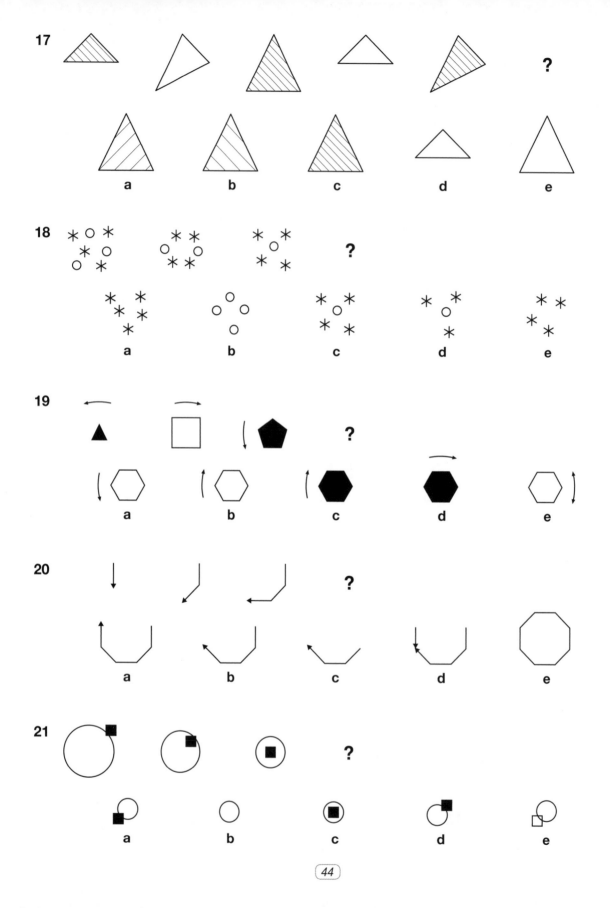

22

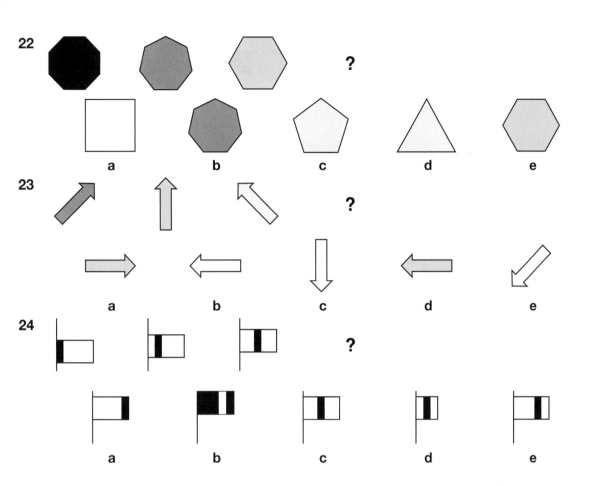

23

24

B 3 Which shape or pattern on the right completes the second pair in the same way as the first pair? Circle the letter.

Example

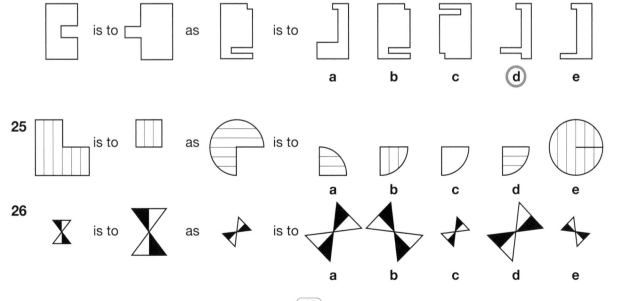

25

26

45

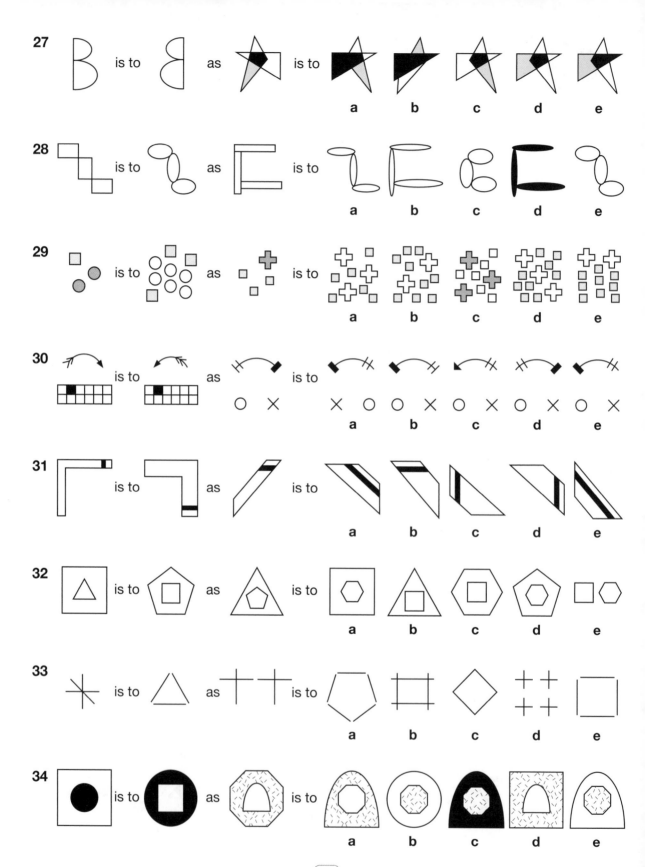

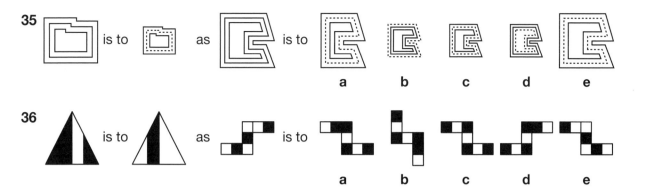

35 is to as is to

a   b   c   d   e

36 is to as is to

a   b   c   d   e

[B 7] Which shape on the right is the reflection of the shape given on the left? Circle the letter.

Example

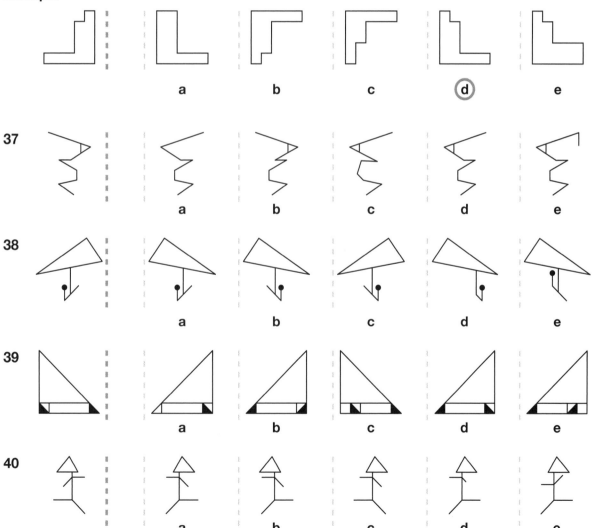

a   b   c   (d)   e

37

a   b   c   d   e

38

a   b   c   d   e

39

a   b   c   d   e

40

a   b   c   d   e

41

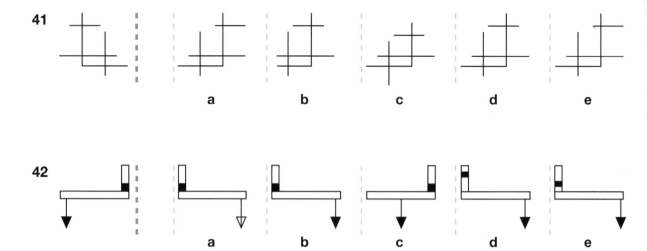

a   b   c   d   e

42

a   b   c   d   e

B 9   Which code matches the shape or pattern given at the end of each line?
Circle the letter.

Example

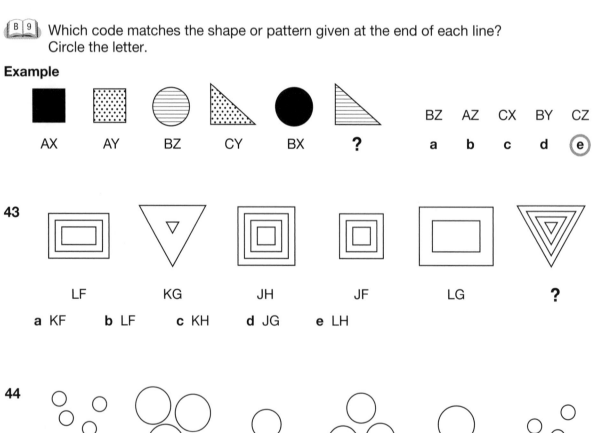

AX   AY   BZ   CY   BX   **?**

BZ   AZ   CX   BY   CZ

a   b   c   d   (e)

43

LF   KG   JH   JF   LG   **?**

a KF   **b** LF   **c** KH   **d** JG   **e** LH

44

EX   FY   DZ   FZ   DY   **?**

a DX   **b** EZ   **c** EY   **d** FX   **e** DZ

45

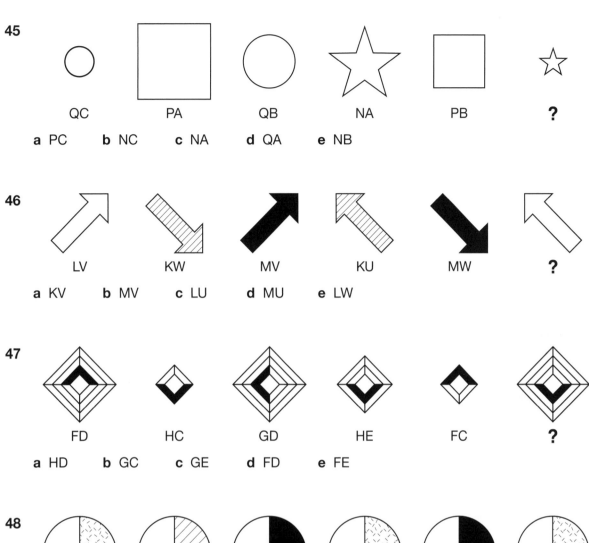

QC   PA   QB   NA   PB   ?

a PC   **b** NC   **c** NA   **d** QA   **e** NB

46

LV   KW   MV   KU   MW   ?

a KV   **b** MV   **c** LU   **d** MU   **e** LW

47

FD   HC   GD   HE   FC   ?

a HD   **b** GC   **c** GE   **d** FD   **e** FE

48

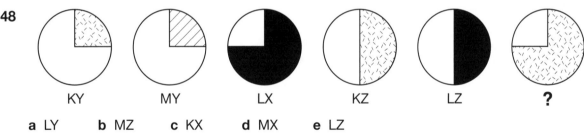

KY   MY   LX   KZ   LZ   ?

a LY   **b** MZ   **c** KX   **d** MX   **e** LZ

Which cube cannot be made from the given net? Circle the letter.

Example

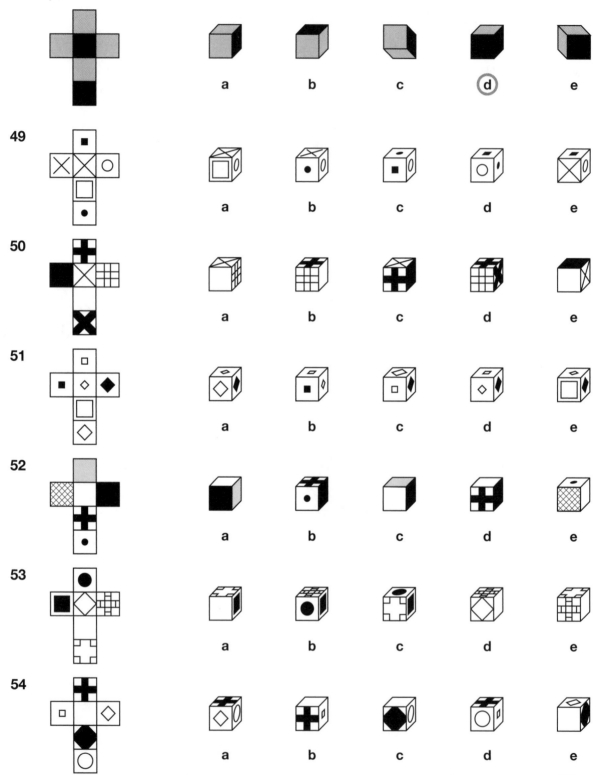

49

a b c d e

50

a b c d e

51

a b c d e

52

a b c d e

53

a b c d e

54

a b c d e

Paper 6

B 1 Which is the odd one out? Circle the letter.

Example

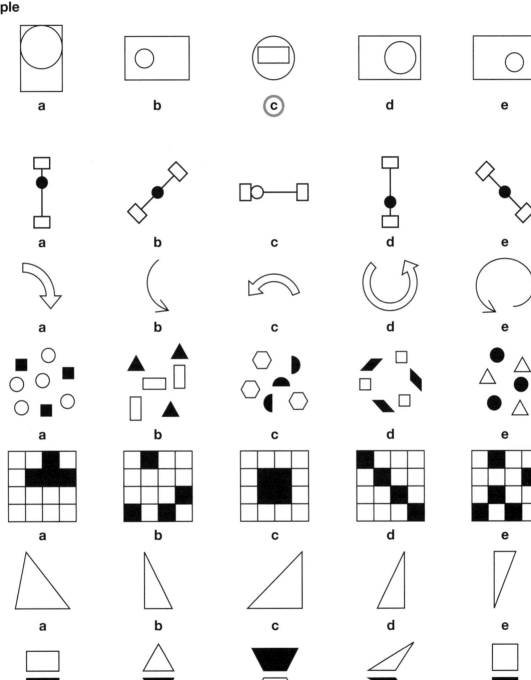

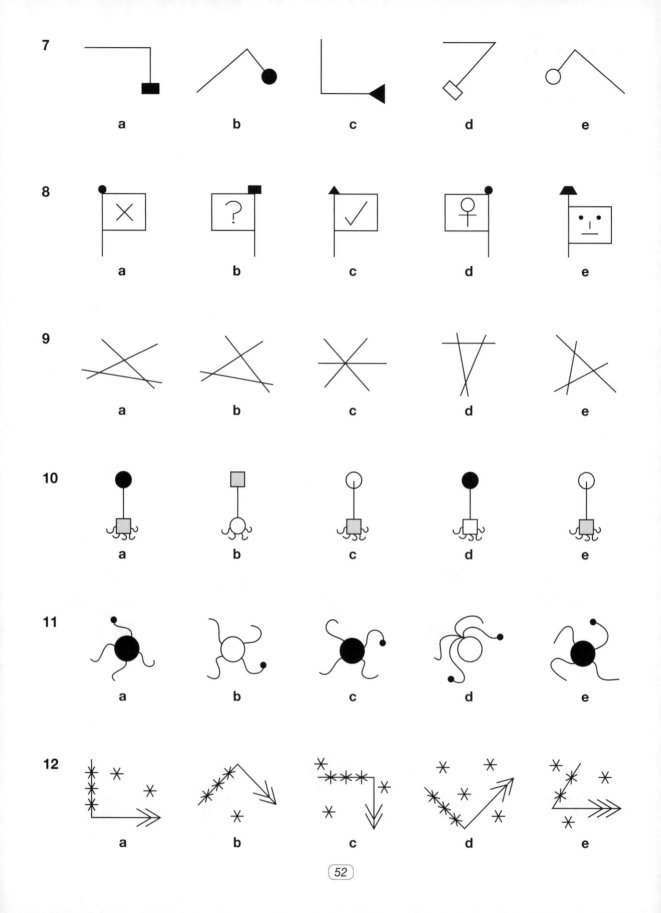

7
    a   b   c   d   e

8
    a   b   c   d   e

9
    a   b   c   d   e

10
    a   b   c   d   e

11
    a   b   c   d   e

12
    a   b   c   d   e

Which one comes next? Circle the letter.

Example

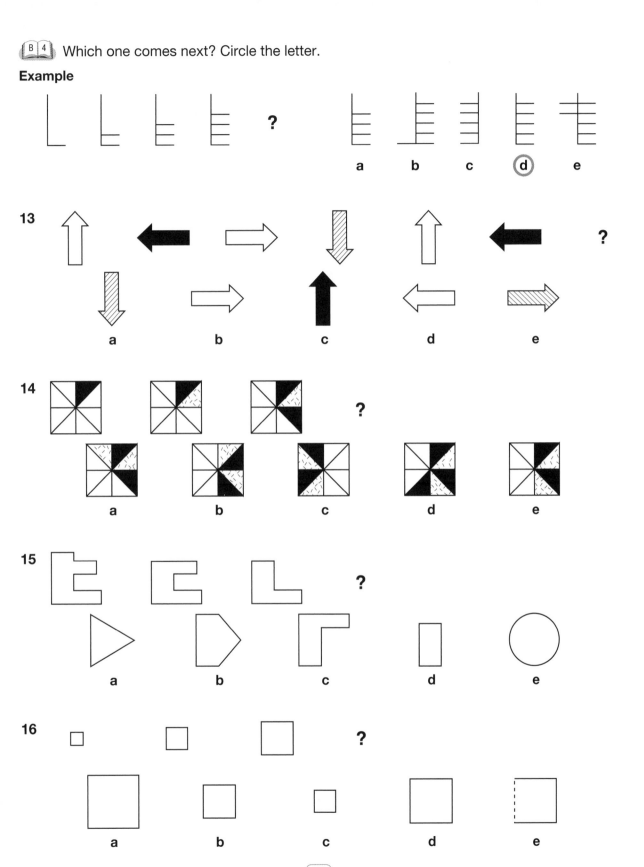

13

14

15

16

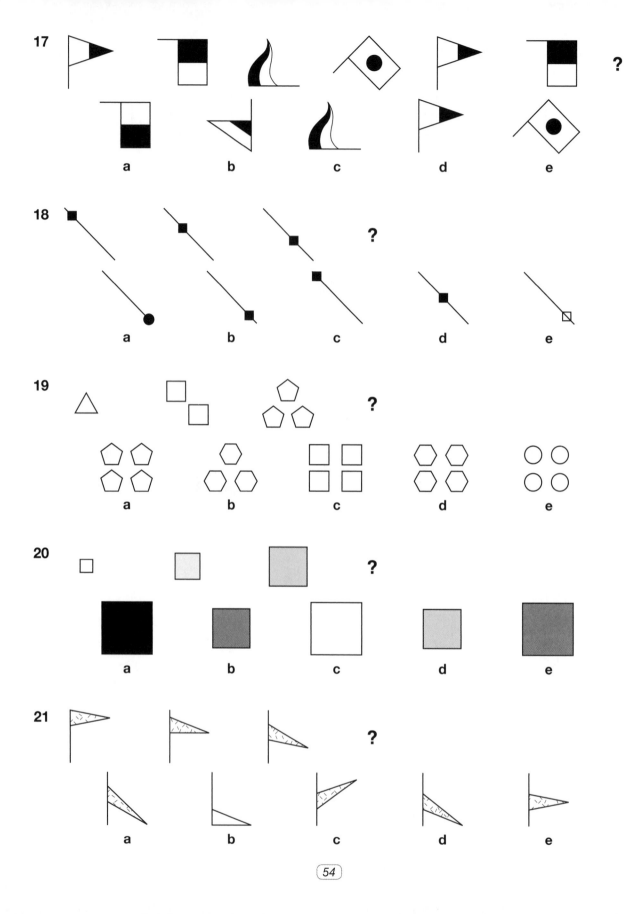

17

a b c d e

18

a b c d e

19

a b c d e

20

a b c d e

21

a b c d e

22

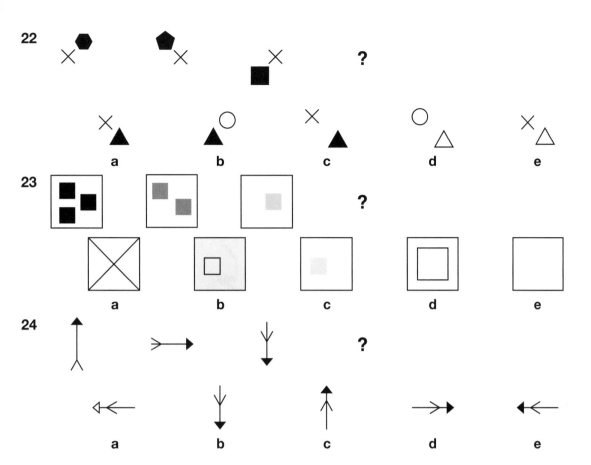

23

24

B 3 Which shape or pattern on the right completes the second pair in the same way as the first pair? Circle the letter.

Example

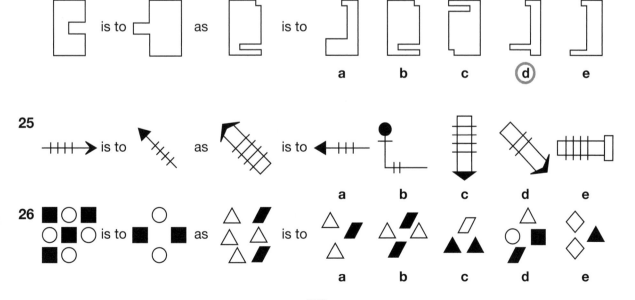

25

26

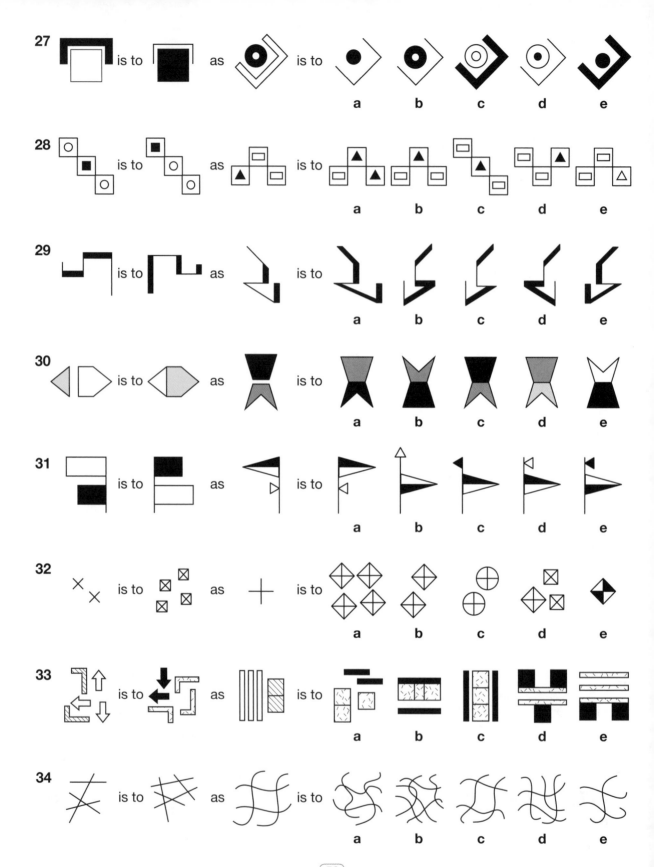

35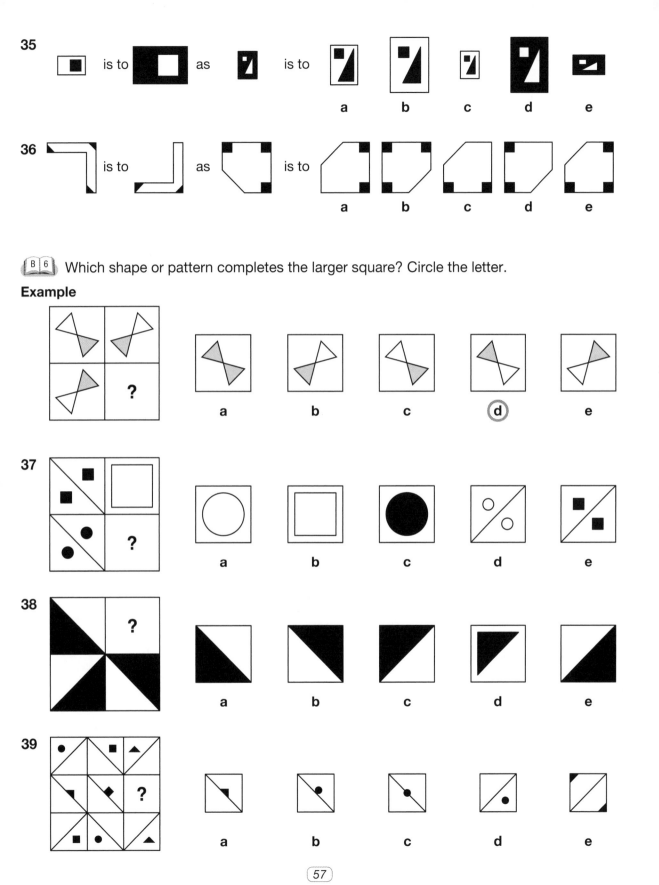

is to ▢ as ▧ is to ...

       a   b   c   d   e

36

is to ... as ... is to ...

       a   b   c   d   e

B 6 Which shape or pattern completes the larger square? Circle the letter.

Example

       a   b   c   (d)   e

37

       a   b   c   d   e

38

       a   b   c   d   e

39

       a   b   c   d   e

40

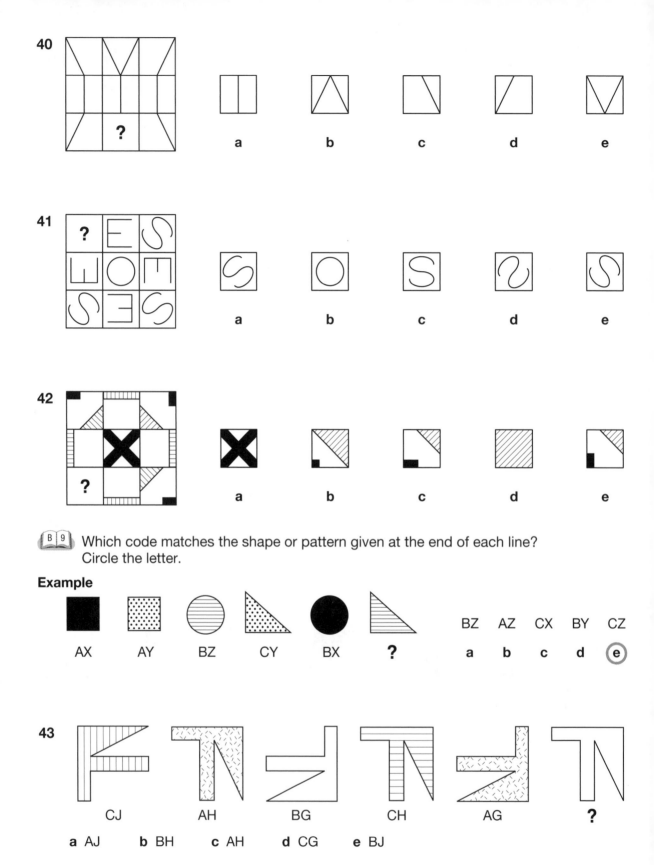

a   b   c   d   e

41

a   b   c   d   e

42

a   b   c   d   e

B 9 Which code matches the shape or pattern given at the end of each line? Circle the letter.

Example

AX   AY   BZ   CY   BX   ?

BZ AZ CX BY CZ

a b c d (e)

43

CJ   AH   BG   CH   AG   ?

a AJ   **b** BH   **c** AH   **d** CG   **e** BJ

44

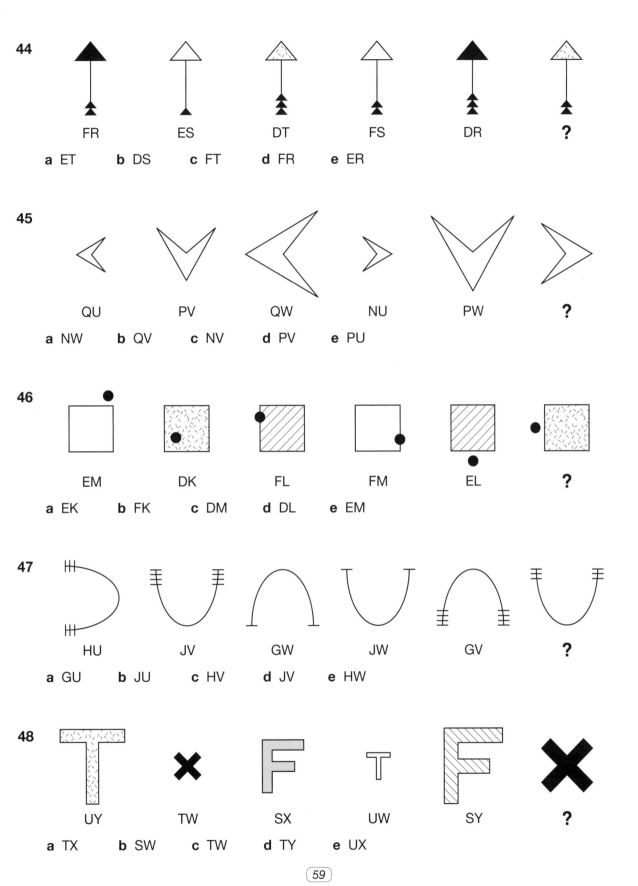

FR ES DT FS DR ?

a ET   **b** DS   **c** FT   **d** FR   **e** ER

45

QU PV QW NU PW ?

a NW   **b** QV   **c** NV   **d** PV   **e** PU

46

EM DK FL FM EL ?

a EK   **b** FK   **c** DM   **d** DL   **e** EM

47

HU JV GW JW GV ?

a GU   **b** JU   **c** HV   **d** JV   **e** HW

48

UY TW SX UW SY ?

a TX   **b** SW   **c** TW   **d** TY   **e** UX

Which shape or pattern is made when the first two shapes or patterns are put together? Circle the letter.

Example

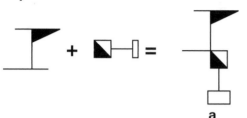 + 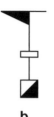 =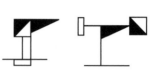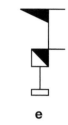

a   b   **ⓒ**   d   e

49

a   b   c   d   e

50

a   b   c   d   e

51

a   b   c   d   e

52

a   b   c   d   e

53

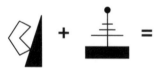

a   b   c   d   e

54

a   b   c   d   e

Progress Chart

Non-verbal Reasoning Assessment Papers 9–10 years Book 1

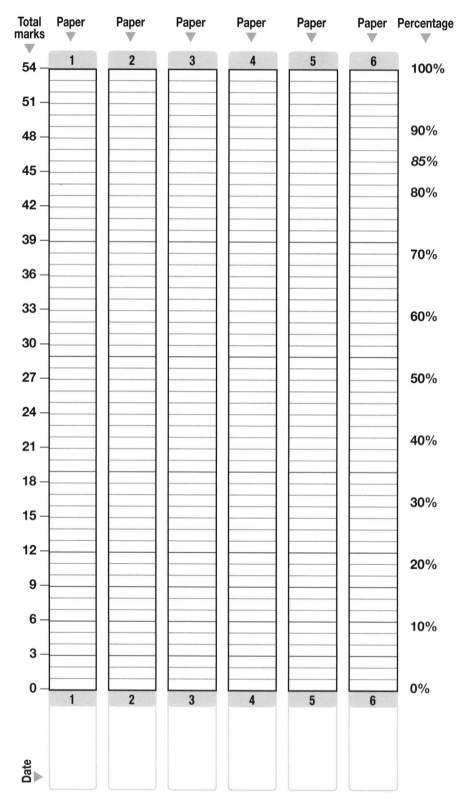

Total marks	Paper 1	Paper 2	Paper 3	Paper 4	Paper 5	Paper 6	Percentage
54	1	2	3	4	5	6	100%
51							
48							90%
45							85% / 80%
42							
39							70%
36							
33							60%
30							
27							50%
24							
21							40%
18							
15							30%
12							20%
9							
6							10%
3							
0	1	2	3	4	5	6	0%

Date ▶

When you've finished the book use the *Next Steps Planner* ➡